THE ILLUSTRATED NATURAL HISTORY OF CANADA

Scientific Consultants to the Series:

The Canadian Shield BARBARA MOON

Earth Science Consultant WALTER TOVELL, Curator, Department of Geology, Royal Ontario Museum. *Life Science Consultant* J. MURRAY SPEIRS, Department of Zoology, University of Toronto

Library of Congress Catalog Card Number: 76-109050

N.S.L. Natural Science of Canada Limited
58 Northline Road, Toronto 16, Ontario, Canada

Publisher: Jack McClelland
Managing Editor: Michael Worek
Assistant Editor: Dorothy Martins
Art Director: William Fox
Visual Editor: Bill Brooks

Editorial Consultant: Pierre Berton

THE CANADIAN SHIELD

Art Director: William Fox
Artists: Vlasta van Kampen
Gordon McLean/Huntley Brown
Gus Fantuz/Jerry Kozoriz

Page 1: A solitary hawk-owl perches on a tree trunk.
Pages 2/3: Minute green discs of duckweed float freely on the water.
Pages 4/5: The many northern lakes etch a peaceful vista.

Contents

Prologue

The author enjoying a recent field trip to the region.

A SENSE OF WILDERNESS

Like the sea, some landforms have a metaphysical force. Great deserts have this force, and mountains, and it is generally accepted in the human community that a spiritual relationship can exist between these places and the men who choose, or are chosen, to live with them.

There are a number of people who believe that the Canadian Shield is such a landform. Certainly something in the country's geography has a grip on the subliminal consciousness of its citizens, so that if you know what to look for there is no way of mistaking a Canadian for any other kind of national. Just as some nations are vikings, and some are mountain-men, and some are riders of the plains, and Americans are frontiersmen, Canadians are a Shield race. Their land incorporates the buttress of the continent, and they live with this permanent reminder of elemental process. They live with bedrock and bush and a million hidden lakes always at their backs. They live with a greedy secret of riches. They live with a vast waste space. They live with the terrifying Boreal, god of the cold void.

It is no accident that critic Northrop Frye should have singled out, as the distinctive quality of English-Canadian verse, the tragic sense of primitive terror. Thus Ned Pratt, on the subject of the Shield presence: "On the North Shore a reptile lay asleep, a hybrid that the myths might have conceived, but not delivered . . . she was too old for death, too old for life . . . ." It is much the same with the poets of Quebec. In either language the images are those of upwrenched frozen roots, cold deep lakes, twisted trees, scarred land, ice, emptiness, predation, wind and stone.

But there are more workaday expressions of the shared cultural subconsciousness. It doesn't matter whether a Canadian has ever been near the Shield or not: he knows the word *muskeg*. And he knows *toboggan* and *shanty*; *hackmatack* and *firebreak*; *canoe* and *high-grade* and *whisky-jack* and *portage* and all the other words that this unique and difficult terrain has supplied to the language.

The Shield has irrevocably shaped Canadian history, influenced the course of Canadian politics and dominated Canadian commerce. The Shield has dictated exploration and settlement patterns, transportation patterns, poverty patterns, and patterns of internal alliance and alienation. The Shield has kept the country half-empty. The Shield has made it physically hard to be one nation. It is possible to love the Shield, or hate it; to be fascinated by it, or repelled. And it is certainly possible to avoid it or forget it and not to be precisely sure what and where it is. But it is not possible to live for long in this country and remain unaffected, for better or worse, by its rock-ribbed imminence. Vincent Massey once wrote, "Geography, perhaps more than the influence of the churches, has made us puritans."

The Shield is bedrock, the primal stuff. This is one of the things a Canadian knows – without perhaps even knowing he knows it.

THE CANADIAN SHIELD:
AN ALBUM
OF MAPS

The maps on the following pages were especially commissioned
for the series. The boundaries above refer to the area treated
in the text and do not indicate the entire Canadian Shield.

*The photograph on the next
two pages shows the area as seen
from a satellite high above the earth.*

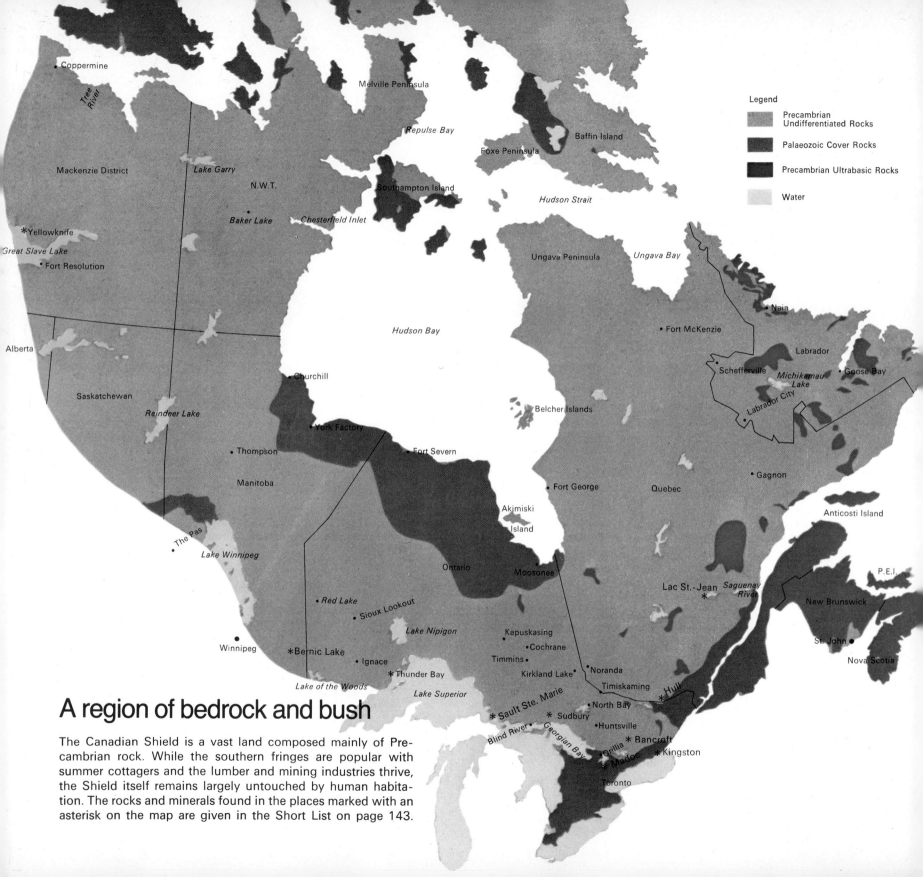

A region of bedrock and bush

The Canadian Shield is a vast land composed mainly of Pre-cambrian rock. While the southern fringes are popular with summer cottagers and the lumber and mining industries thrive, the Shield itself remains largely untouched by human habitation. The rocks and minerals found in the places marked with an asterisk on the map are given in the Short List on page 143.

Legend

Precambrian Undifferentiated Rocks

Palaeozoic Cover Rocks

Precambrian Ultrabasic Rocks

Water

Life on the Shield

Note: The maps (centre) indicate the breeding ranges and habitats of the animal life listed below.

Northern pike may reach a length of 4 feet, and are common fish in many Shield lakes.

Perch, favourite game fish which make excellent eating, are abundant in lakes and large streams.

Spruce budworms are injurious forest insects, feeding heavily on balsam fir and spruce buds.

Mancinus butterflies add their delicate beauty to northern areas during the summer.

Caribou are well adapted to life on the tundra; their broad hoofs enable them to travel on snow or muskeg.

White-tailed deer, a favourite prey of wolves, usually roam in young forest environments.

Black ducks, found at the edge of ponds, marshes and lakes, nest in woodland areas.

Moose, found all over the Shield, live in the densely forested areas and usually near shallow lakes.

Goldeneyes, called "whistlers" because of the sound made by their wings, are found along lakeshores.

Sharp-tailed grouse, widely misnamed "prairie chickens," are found from Alaska to Quebec.

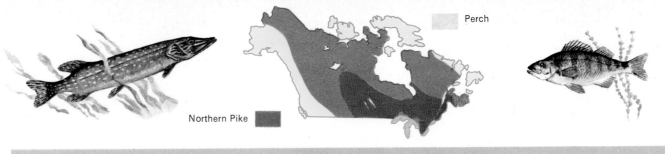

Northern Pike | Perch

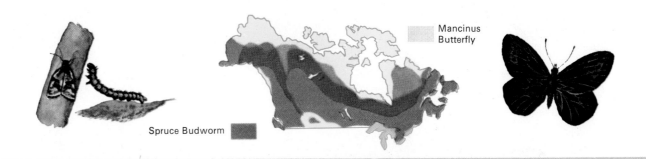

Spruce Budworm | Mancinus Butterfly

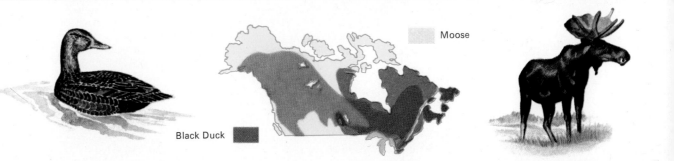

Caribou | White-tailed Deer

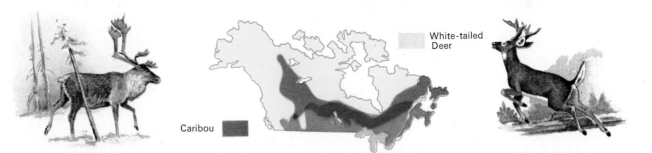

Black Duck | Moose

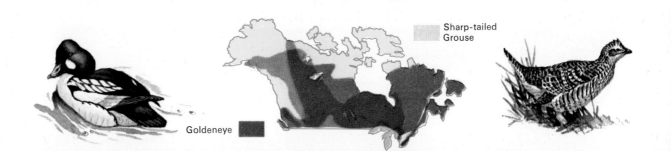

Goldeneye | Sharp-tailed Grouse

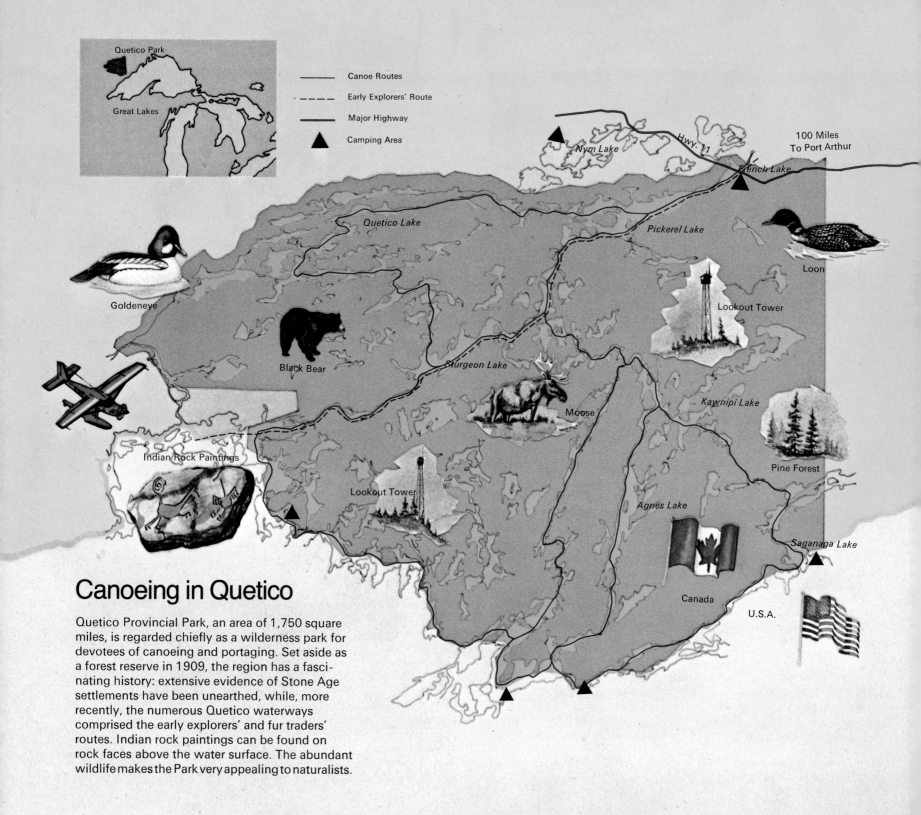

Quetico Park

Great Lakes

Canoe Routes
Early Explorers' Route
Major Highway
Camping Area

Nym Lake

Hwy. 11

French Lake

100 Miles
To Port Arthur

Quetico Lake

Pickerel Lake

Loon

Lookout Tower

Goldeneye

Black Bear

Sturgeon Lake

Kawnipi Lake

Moose

Pine Forest

Indian Rock Paintings

Lookout Tower

Agnes Lake

Saganaga Lake

Canada

U.S.A.

Canoeing in Quetico

Quetico Provincial Park, an area of 1,750 square
miles, is regarded chiefly as a wilderness park for
devotees of canoeing and portaging. Set aside as
a forest reserve in 1909, the region has a fascinating history: extensive evidence of Stone Age
settlements have been unearthed, while, more
recently, the numerous Quetico waterways
comprised the early explorers' and fur traders'
routes. Indian rock paintings can be found on
rock faces above the water surface. The abundant
wildlife makes the Park very appealing to naturalists.

Adventure in Algonquin

Algonquin Provincial Park, situated on a southern extension of the Canadian Shield, comprises an area of about 2,900 square miles. Erosion and glaciation have reshaped this once mountainous country, forming a rolling, hilly upland which is higher than the surrounding land. The forested wilderness of Algonquin Park is home to a great many birds and mammals not normally seen so close to civilization, and the numerous hiking trails in the Park interior are excellent for nature study. Perhaps the best way to see the interior is to travel by canoe on the hundreds of water routes winding through the wilderness, but trips are also possible by automobile (Highway 60, across the southern end), by rail (C.N.R. operating between North Bay and Ottawa) and by aircraft (landings restricted to certain lakes). A summer staff of naturalists is on hand to conduct a programme of evening talks and guided hikes, and some points of interest in a southern section of the Park are pinpointed below. The main highway and a few roads used for logging are open year round, and in winter some areas are ideal for snowshoeing. This, too, is the season to see winter birds and evidence of non-hibernating animals.

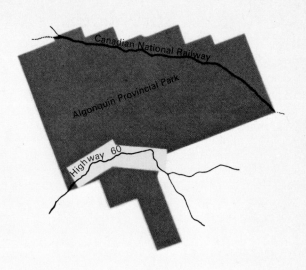

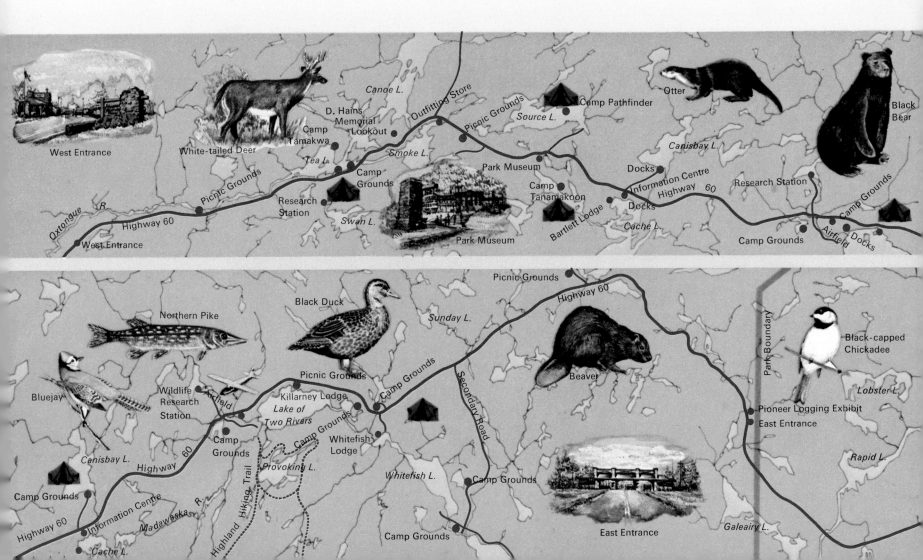

Parc des Laurentides

The Laurentides Park region, created in 1895, covers an area of 3,710 square miles. Undoubtedly the principal reason behind the establishment of the Park was to assure the survival of the caribou; despite an early abundance, the species has largely disappeared, though efforts are now being made to re-introduce the animal to its former habitat.

to Chicoutimi

Lac St-Jean

R. Saguenay

R. St-Laurent

to Lac St-Jean

R. Chicoutimi

Hwy 54

Le Gite du Berger

R. Métabetchouan

Black Duck

Hwy 54A

Lac Montagnais

Barrière Kiskissink

Lac Métascouac

Depot des Ecorces

Hwy 56

Lac St-Henri

R. Malboie

Moose

Grand Lac
Jacques-Cartier

to St-Urbain

Parc des Laurentides

R. des Brûlés

Black Bear

R. Jacques-Cartier

to Québec

Barrière Stoneham

Woodcock

Legend:

▲ Major Camp or Inn

Fishing Areas

Main Highways

PART ONE / THE REGION

1 HALF THE COUNTRY

The Canadian Shield has been called the most important physical feature of the North American continent, though it was a Canadian geologist who said it, and he may be thought prejudiced. But the Shield certainly has to be the over-riding physical fact of Canada: it is half the country.

Geologically, the Shield is that extended area in which Precambrian rock is exposed at the surface or lies just underneath a thin cover of weathered litter and vegetation. Precambrian rock is rock that was formed between the time the earth's crust first cooled and the time when organic life was far enough advanced to leave fossil evidence of its presence. It represents the first three billion years of earth's geological history. Compared to this span of time the rearing of all the world's charted mountain chains, the development of the familiar continental profiles, the rise and spread of all land vegetation, the formation of the fossil fuels like coal and oil that power modern life, and the evolution of the whole vertebrate order including man, are the crowding events of recent history. Even the youngest Precambrian rock is older than any of these.

Most of the Shield rock, about eighty per cent, is what is called banded gneiss: a coarsely crystalline rock of varying composition but with its own special texture. The constituent minerals in gneiss have differentiated and drawn themselves out into more or less separate ribbons and streaks. This is the badge of deep burial within the earth, perhaps fifteen miles down under heat and extreme directed pressure so that the minerals rearranged themselves along the planes of maximum relief from stress. If all the rock that makes up all the land areas of the world were dumped together and buried under such pressure that it began to mingle and fuse, the result would be a streaky porridge very like this Shield rock. As for its composition, it is an abstraction made concrete: the average building material of the continents.

This same sort of Precambrian rock underlies much, if not all, of the rest of North America; it forms a so-called "basement" under the thick modern sediments of the plains and prairies; where the mighty Grand Canyon slices through a mile of these

sediments, Precambrian rock can be seen at the very base. And it has been caught up and raised aloft, along with new rock and thick slabs of sediments, in the Appalachians of the eastern continental margin, and the fringing Cordillera of the west.

But here in the Shield it is not just a hidden foundation but the stronghold itself. It is a vast ellipse arching from the Atlantic on the east to the Arctic Sea in the far northwest, and looping back through the high Arctic and Baffin Islands to the long bleak coast of Labrador, all but a sliver of Quebec, all but the southwestern wedge of Ontario, more than half of Manitoba, about half of Saskatchewan, a corner of Alberta, all of the districts of Mackenzie and Keewatin, the Franklin mainland, and 196,000 square miles of Arctic islands. It is about two million square miles in area – or half the Canadian land mass. The total Shield area is actually about 100,000 square miles more than this, for it thrusts a lobe, the Adirondacks, into upstate New York by way of the Thousand Islands, and it extends south and west beyond Lake Superior into Michigan, Wisconsin and Minnesota. Most Canadian maps of the Shield pretend that it stops at the Canadian border.

In relief, the Shield is a crudely saucer-shaped upland plateau. Before the end of Precambrian time the process of erosion had brought all surfaces equally to the level of the sea. But now the plain stands, on average, 1500 feet above sea level. The whole mass seems to have been uplifted several times, and in the course of recurrent uplift and subsidence the Shield has been warped so that now the edges are higher than the middle. Hudson Bay, occupying what seems to be a zone of old crustal weakness, is in the centre – the depression in the saucer. Other than these enigmatic vertical movements, the Shield has been exempt from major geological events, such as mountain-building, since the Precambrian era. It has been what geologists call "stable."

The word "shield" was coined in 1892 by the Austrian geologist, Eduard Suess, to describe just such stable continental blocks of more or less exposed Precambrian rock. Every continent seemed to have at least one, and it seemed to Suess that their shape and contour was that of a buckler, and that they were the tough core around which later formations had been assembled, and against which later geologic events had spent themselves. It was a rather romantic notion, and apt to be misleading, but the term has stuck.

There are shield areas in South America (the Guyanan-Brazilian Shield), in Scandinavia (the Baltic Shield) and in Siberia (the Angara Shield); most of peninsular India, all of Africa south of the Sahara, a third of Australia and probably half of Antarctica are broadly classified as shield areas as well. But among them all the Canadian Shield is unique, for the four glacial advances of the recent Ice Age scraped its whole vast surface clean. In the shields of the southern hemisphere, the Precambrian bedrock is still cloaked with the suave soil and cover of the millenia: by ancient veldt or abiding jungle or shifting sand or south polar ice; even where there are outcrops, the old rock often carries a veneer of younger formations. In the northern hemisphere, the Baltic Shield was also scraped clean during the Ice Age, but it is a much smaller area than the Canadian Shield; and the Angara Shield of Siberia was only lightly glaciated in comparison.

But in North America, the Canadian Shield was the very hub of the glaciation. At its highest, the ice-cap must have been something like two miles thick; and, though the whole northern half of the continent was gripped by ice, this maximum thickness was centred over what is now the District of Keewatin and over the northern part of New Quebec, the two centres bracketing Hudson Bay. The downward pressure exerted by two miles of ice is approximately nine billion tons per square mile of land surface. It is certainly enough pressure to render the lower ice layers plastic and to start glacial creep. And with boulders and rock fragments and abrasive granules frozen in the bottom surface, it was certainly enough pressure for the advancing ice to bite through the old Shield cover of vegetation, soil, subsoil, weathered and decaying rock into the living bone. The Shield was ground down to Precambrian bedrock as the ice-cap advanced.

When the ice retreated, it left behind such a rubbish of rock litter, of roiled gravel and broken stone and boulders, as to scar the terrain with the great oblong dumps that are called drumlins and the snaking rubble embankments that are called eskers; as to fill in whole valleys and clefts and depressions; as to derange the drainage into the merest haphazard sort of surface run-off.

The ice left the Shield a barren and sterile landscape. Though time, even so short a time as the seven or eight thousand years since the last Ice Age has begun to mend the Shield, it remains the largest raw area of exposed Precambrian rock in the world.

2 FORBIDDING TERRAIN

There are some people for whom the Shield, like the austerity of ancient faces, is very beautiful and exciting. In the high northeast of Labrador there are mountains; the Torngats. They are not proper mountains, being only the upwarped Shield rim deeply dissected into chasms and peaks, but the highest peak, Cirque Mountain, rises to almost six thousand feet. All along the Labrador coast there are long fiords, hanging valleys, and rugged islands separated from the shore by narrow, deep channels. Farther south and inland from the sea, the Churchill River plunges into a gorge in a clear fall of more than three hundred feet, twice the height of Niagara, with a roar that can be heard for ten miles around. Both sound and sight have such chilling power that upland and lowland Indians avoid the place in superstition.

Along most of the north shore of the St. Lawrence the Shield is a brooding grey presence that looms over the river; at Cap Tourmente the river swings away south though, and leaves the Shield standing off in the distance like a low roll of leaden cloud on the horizon. Between Gananoque and Kingston the Shield is a set of stepping-stones across the St. Lawrence: the low, evergreen-clad hummocks of the Thousand Islands.

Across central Ontario to Lake Huron and beyond, the Shield is the familiar cottage country, and north of Lake Superior it is an endless stretch of Christmas trees and glinting water seen from a train window.

At Lake Winnipeg begins the great northwestern sweep to the Arctic Sea, and strung all along this perimeter is a striking group of large lakes lying just in the contact between the Precambrian rocks and the younger formations of the plains. They were formed by glacial meltwater backed up and trapped against the bulwark of the Shield.

The first of them is Lake Winnipeg itself, long known as the roughest lake in North America. Old-timers on the lake claim that its vile temperament is somehow an effect produced by the Shield gneiss on the east shore in confrontation with the prairie limestone on the west. After Lake Winnipeg comes Lake Athabasca, and then Great Slave and Great Bear, and then the Shield

edge strikes north across the tundra to the coast. To those who love it, every part of the great Shield perimeter has its own comeliness. But in many ways the Shield is an appalling place.

When Leif Ericson missed his way home to Greenland in 995 A.D. and came instead upon the wild, bleak Labrador coast, he could think of nothing to christen his landfall but Helluland – "the land of flat stones." Considerably later, James Audubon, the naturalist, landed on the same coast, stepped on what he thought were rocks, sank nearly up to his knees in muskeg, and wrote tartly in his journal: "Not a square foot of *earth* could we see. A poor rugged miserable country."

Jacques Cartier, sailing up the St. Lawrence, gazed at the cold grey bluffs that line the north shore and decided it was "the land God gave to Cain." He reported to the King of France, "there isn't a cartload of dirt in the whole of it."

On the other side of the Shield, Samuel Hearne made an epic journey from Hudson Bay over the tundra to the Coppermine River and the Arctic coast in 1771-72 and wrote later, "the land throughout the whole tract of country is scarcely anything but one solid mass of rocks and stones." He named it the Barren Ground.

More recently, in 1928, a Nevadan prospector spent three months up Rouyn way and wrote disgustedly to a friend in Wallace, Idaho, "I found out one thing, that if a prospector can't find a mine in America, he will not better himself by going to Canada, for that is the hardest in the world to get into and look for a mine. It is the toughest country I was ever in."

There has been a good deal more to the same effect, and if it seems to consist of sweeping generalizations, that is only to be expected. The Shield itself is a sweeping generalization – or a series of them. A man set down in the Keewatin tundra could scarcely tell he was not in Ungava. A man who steps from his own back door to stroll in the Kenora bush could be anywhere in a dark forest that stretches for 3,500 miles. The knowing eye may see complexity and local variety in the typical landscapes, but the Shield is so vast that each of them seems to go on to infinity. There is a primitive terror in this sort of magnitude. The landscapes of the Shield are dictated by the landform itself, and

Scraped and sliced down to the base rock by glacial advances in the Ice Ages, the contours of the Shield are still being shaped by ice and cold.

by the climate. The climate is what is called a continental climate, with severe temperatures and a relatively low annual rainfall. The mean precipitation in the tundra is a scant fifteen inches a year, and throughout most of the Shield's great midsection it is no more than forty inches. By its position, the Shield is cut off from any of the great warming ocean currents, and its centre is occupied by a large shallow body of water that freezes over in winter. And, of course, it was the centre of glaciation in the last Ice Age; continuous or patchy permafrost still underlies not only the whole tundra but large areas south of the treeline as well.

These are the reasons usually given for the great climatic warp that can be seen on any general meteorological map of the continent. In effect, polar and subarctic climates are displaced southward over the whole main mass of the Shield. There are greater extremes of cold just north of Lake Superior than up in the Mackenzie Delta. Indeed, in a crude way the warp echoes the outline of the Shield and this, in turn, has an extraordinary effect. For the transcontinental vegetational zones echo the climatic warp and sag southward too, as if to accommodate the Shield. Thus most of the tundra is centred in the eastern Arctic, on the Shield. The treeline, which approaches the Arctic coast near the Mackenzie Delta, makes a festoon south around the bottom of Hudson Bay and then curves northeast across Labrador to the Atlantic coast. The southern limit of the boreal forest sags to the edge of the Shield in the same way. The effect is to restrict the Shield to a few great panoramic landscapes.

In the north beyond the treeline, on both sides of Hudson Bay and stretching away to the high Arctic islands, there is the tundra. The ice made its final stand here. Now it is a cruel waste of bedrock and glacial litter, with a permanently frozen substrate, less summer rainfall than parts of the Sahara and only a bitter driven scum of snow in the long winter. Even the gneisses show the effects of snow-blast. The peculiar mechanics of frost-heaving have patterned the terrain with ice-wedge polygons, frost boils and mud circles. A mosaic of lichens makes a low patchy ground cover, though mosses and stunted plants and deformed and dwarfed trees may grow in favourable locations. The western Arctic beyond the Shield is kinder, and it is customary to talk glowingly of the complex, though dwarfed, vegetation; of the blaze of flowers in the brief Arctic summer; of the prize vegetables that can be coaxed to grow. But here in the Shield the tundra is no more than rock desert.

The treeline is not really a line at all but a transition zone, called the taiga. Here the tundra grades into a bleak subarctic savannah with dark bushy rosettes of dwarfed spruce scattered in clumps and patches over the pale lichen heath. And this in turn grades into the true boreal forest, that has been called the typical landscape of Canada.

The boreal forest is transcontinental, but it broadens to take in the whole vast mid-section of the Shield. The soil is thin and sour, poor skimpy stuff containing so much acid that the vital elements are leached downward out of reach of plant roots, leaving a grey barren horizon just under the surface humus. The experts call it podsol. Anything that roots here must root shallowly, in the humus layer, and must be able to tolerate the acids. And so the forest is dominated by white and black spruce, and in the east by spruce and balsam fir. A few hardwood weed-trees such as birch and aspen have a foothold, too, and flare into second-growth stands after wildfire or logging. And there are willows and alders in the sheltered river bottoms. But for the most part the forest is a dense forbidding monotony of dark conifers. Those who venture into it, on the ground, sometimes speak of an oppressive prickling of the nerve-ends, and an unreasoning urge to flee.

From far northwest through to the Labrador coast the boreal forest is broken only by tracts of muskeg on the low-lying ground. Canada has more muskeg, 500,000 square miles, than all of Russia, and for reasons that have to do with climate and terrain, most of it is here in this zone of the Shield. From the air it can look beautiful: a glinting waterland curving over the horizon, with the sun reflecting from thousands of pools and creeks between which twist delicately coloured strips of land, blue, red, brown, purple. But at ground level it is a treacherous, sucking, ill-smelling bog of peaty muck, spongy sphagnum moss and standing water. And because muskeg creates conditions that foster its own growth, it has sometimes been described as a cancer, eating into healthy land and so increasing itself. The familiar "forest of sticks" of the north usually marks a place where the muskeg is advancing on the forest and has already swamped the spruce on its margins. In any case muskeg is a hazard, both to life and to transport. It has swallowed, among other things, whole sections of railway track, a derailed locomotive in northern Manitoba, and an entire section of highway near Smooth Rock Falls, Ontario.

In the very south-central part of the Shield, in Ontario and Quebec, the landscape changes again. Here the boreal forest grades into the Great Lakes-St. Lawrence forest. It is interrupted by two largish clay belts left by post-glacial lakes, but otherwise the forest is now the familiar and beloved mixture of pines and hemlocks and birches and maples, with shrubs and wild-flowers in the clearings, and beaver-swamps, and busy animal life, and hundreds of clear inviting lakes and streams. This is a much more complex environment than any other on the Shield, and there are many more species of plants and animals than there are farther north, and very many more people. All but a handful of the permanent residents of the Shield live here along the southern margin, in this temperate mixed forest of Ontario and Quebec. And this is camping country as well, the resort of a hundred thousand hunters and fishers and summer holidayers. But though this is the best-known sector of the Shield it is the least part of it, and the least typical.

Yet it shares at least two unifying elements with all the rest of the Shield's great expanse. One is the geology, for everywhere, south to north and east to west, there is the same shaping rock. Beyond the treeline it lies naked except for the lichens. Elsewhere it lies just under the thin sour podsols, and the muskegs and the forests, outcropping for perhaps ten miles in every hundred. But it gives the whole two million square miles the same low relief. And everywhere it has been sculpted by faulting and folding, the special nature of the ancient formations and the differential effects of time into the same two repetitive topographies. One is a long, flat dip-slope that ends in an abrupt drop. Such escarpments can be found everywhere in the Shield. The other is a topography of low rounded domes that the geologists, vividly enough, describe as "mammilated." Both the mammilation and the escarpments are an integral part of the unmistakable Shield "look."

So is the water. In any aerial view, the amount of water lying on the Shield is almost unbelievable. It stands everywhere, like water in a ploughed field after heavy rain. In places it has been estimated to occupy one-third to one-half the surface area. Lakes lie in every rock cup and glacial furrow. Others are retained in glacial debris. Still others are widenings of blocked and baffled river systems. Between and connecting the countless lakes are countless rivers – though most scarcely deserve the name, being little more than surface runoff, or else short steep spillways from one catchment-basin to the next. Even the bigger rivers are often no more than chains of lakes connected by short turbulent stretches where the water takes whatever route it can find. True, the Saguenay River, which drains Lake St. John, has found its way into a deeply incised pre-glacial riverbed and runs into the St. Lawrence, for its last ninety miles, through a gorge that is in places several hundred feet deeper than average tide-level. But more commonly the pre-existing drainage system was choked and blocked by the glaciation, leaving melt-water and rainfall to collect and run off where and how they could.

And, just as integral to the Shield as the rock and the water, are the biting insects. To anyone who has spent a season anywhere on the Shield, the mosquitoes and black flies are part of the memory. They are aquatic insects, spawned of standing and running water and so they reach numbers here that are unthinkable to those who have not seen for themselves. The mosquitoes are the particular plague of the tundra. A man prospecting out of Yellowknife with a companion in the Thirties has left one account. After speaking of the unending organlike hum of the insects through the night, the rattle-like driving rain as they kept hitting the canvas, and the black crawling mass of them that sheathed a hand thrust outside the tent flap, he described the scene at breakfast: "In a few moments the bacon in the frying pan was mottled with hundreds of black dots, flies that had perished. In the coffeepot floated a layer that covered the whole surface. A basin with soapy water would in a few minutes be coated with drowned mosquitoes."

And if mosquitoes are the plague of the tundra, the black flies are the plague of the boreal forest. Black flies are nearly worldwide in distribution, but they reach their greatest numbers here in the boreal forest of the Shield. Indeed there are bush experts who believe that black flies will forever limit the Shield's usefulness. Researchers have estimated at sixteen billion the number of eggs on a fifteen-foot rock outcrop near a waterfall in northern Quebec, and they have counted five million larvae per square meter of riverbed. Other researchers, working north of Baie Comeau, Quebec, have counted an average of 325 black flies per minute landing on a scrap of blue cloth less than a foot square. There are documented cases of black flies literally biting men to death, driving men insane, of black flies in such choking swarms that animals have suffocated by breathing them in.

Bedrock, tundra, taiga, boreal forest, deranged drainage, muskeg, mosquitoes, black flies: add to these a climate that at its worst is arctic and at its best offers only four frost-free months a year. Even as far south as Timmins the yearly average is a mere forty frost-free days. And that is the Shield.

It is a place where people get lost, get bushed, get driven mad by insects in summer, can freeze to death in winter. They can venture across it only in the light, small canoes that the Indians had to invent for the precise purpose. Or they can get around in float planes or helicopters. They can't get far on foot, in cars, in trains, in big powered boats, or in standard aircraft – which is to say in all the forms of transport taken for granted elsewhere. The Shield imposes quite abnormal terms.

3 RICHES IN THE ROCK

The resources of the Canadian Shield have made Canada a rich nation. In the beginning, of course, there were the furs – furs enough to make men forget Cathay. Then there were the fine white pine stands and, when the white pine was logged out, the spruce of the boreal forest to be the mainstay of a giant pulp-and-paper industry. Of the eighteen mills currently taking softwood from Canada's boreal forest, fifteen are on the Shield. Then, in the wake of railway building, there were the first great mineral strikes. No one really knows the rules that govern mineral occurrences except that they are the companion of fresh rock borne from the depths, or else of rock that has been reworked under heat and pressure. Since such rock is its very essence, the

The boreal forest stetches across Canada in a wide belt that averages six hundred miles in width, dominated mainly by white and black spruce trees. The vast area of this forest provides a wealth of timber and a sanctuary for many vanishing forms of wildlife.

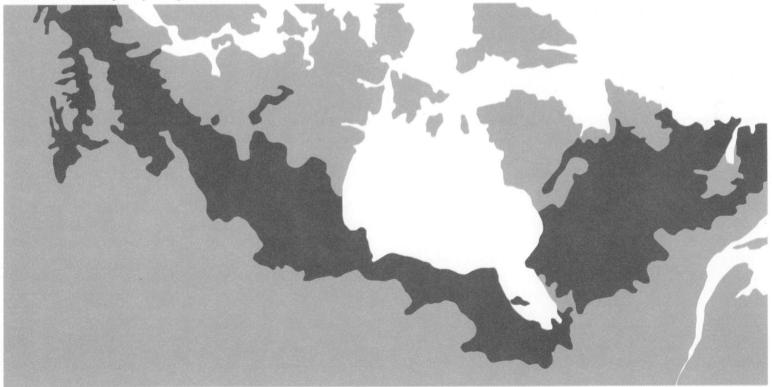

Shield is a mineral treasure-chest – gold, silver, nickel, copper, uranium, iron, asbestos, and more. Mineral production from the Shield is on the order of a billion dollars a year. Now there is hydro-electric power to add to the tally of riches. Rivers in the Shield are currently generating some thirteen million kilowatts of power. By 1974, when the nine power plants on the Manicouaga-Outardes Rivers are operating at full strength, another 5,800,000 kilowatts will have been added to the total; and even so, the undeveloped hydro potential of the Shield is estimated to be something like twenty-five million kilowatts. And yet, for all the booty, it is a simple, large truth that the presence of the Shield warps the whole pattern of life in Canada.

Back in 1878 a certain Captain Twining, reporting on the situation of the Red River settlements in Manitoba, wrote about the Shield: "This region of swamps and sterile pinelands has imposed an effectual barrier to communications towards the Canadas, and has forced the traffic of these remote settlements to find an outlet through Minnesota." Indeed the midwestern Americans had already begun to think of the Canadian prairies as their own rich natural hinterland. The Canadian politicians, finally, couldn't brook this casual American expansionism and forsook the tempting southern route to forge the Canadian Pacific railway straight across the Shield. But the Shield was where the whole railway scheme nearly foundered; in the end the crews had to blast their way across a thousand miles of rock from Sudbury to Schreiber with dynamite made on the spot.

In the same way, settlement has avoided the Shield unless driven to it by expediency. In 1969 Cecil King, the former head of an English newspaper empire, wrote in his memoirs, "Canada is not a country: it is the northern fringe of the United States. It looks huge on the map, but when you get there you find that the country is 5,000 miles long and only 200 miles wide. The rest is uninhabited desert."

Nine-tenths of the people of Canada occupy considerably less than half its space. Most of the nine-tenths are crowded down into the slivers and wedges of land along the international boundary from the Atlantic coast to past the centre of the continent. That is because nine-tenths of the people of Canada choose to avoid the Shield. As soon as the pressure of the Shield presence is removed in western Manitoba and Saskatchewan, the population spreads up and out to occupy the rich arable land of the prairies. Population density maps outline the profile of the Shield with almost ludicrous fidelity.

So do the land-use maps. In the agricultural sense, the Shield is a desert. There are 700,000 or so acres being farmed on glacial clay in the Lake St. John region of Quebec, and a million and a quarter acres in the clay belts across the Ontario-Quebec border. Aside from these and a few fertile patches along the rivers, the Shield is no place for farmers. The gullible settlers who grabbed up land grants in the eastern counties of Ontario found that out to their cost. The Shield shook them off and starved them out. The most familiar sight in the area today is the abandoned, stoney little upland farm reclaimed by bush.

But the most revealing maps of all are the transportation maps. The travel routes in the Shield are those of the raiding party: in for the booty and right back out again. Aside from the politically obligatory transcontinental railways, only two railways on the Shield go anywhere in the accepted sense of the term: the Hudson Bay Railway provides transport from The Pas, Manitoba, to Churchill on Hudson Bay. The Ontario Northland goes to Moosonee on James Bay. Any others are mere spur lines to exploit specific resources.

As for roads: Labrador is empty of them, and the most northern points served by road in Quebec and Ontario are Chibougamau, Red Lake, Pickle Crow and Nakina. Roads in Manitoba skirt the Shield edge, but only one ventures any distance on it: the road goes to Thompson and it is gravel. One road in the district of Mackenzie connects Yellowknife with Mackay Lake. And that is about all. The pattern of movement is deflected around the periphery. It is as though the Shield were a whirlpool interrupting the mainstream of normal traffic.

And so it is. Even the exploitation of resources has followed no normal south-to-north pattern, no orderly pushing back of the Arctic frontier. Instead development has sidled east or northwest along the perimeters, from a nucleus in the south-central Shield. From the St. Lawrence through to the Lake of the Woods the pulp mills and lumber camps huddle near transport and

Slow, meandering streams like this one are a common sight on the Shield. In the many areas where drainage is poor, the water flows sluggishly through boggy stretches of extremely absorbent muskeg.

civilization. From Labrador City to Yellowknife, the miners mine only the accessible margins.

Perhaps if the Shield were a desert or a sea, people would better understand its nature and influence, and its peculiar, centrifugal, shaping force. But as it is, and quite extraordinarily, most Canadians don't seem to grasp the physical fact of the Shield at all. They have no idea of its extent, talk of it vaguely as being "up North" somewhere, the Laurentian Highlands maybe, or Muskoka – and, oh yes, of course, the Lake Superior North Shore.

Editorial writers delight in making odious comparisons between the Soviet development of Siberia and the Canadian performance in the north, as though facing up to permafrost were the only problem. Politicians talk of "the vision of the north" and "road to resources" as though the roads were easy and the vision attainable, given enough capital – and thermal underwear.

A famous North American naturalist was even capable, recently, of writing about the Shield as though it only occurred east of James Bay. He lumped the rest of it in with the Northwest Territories and called it "the great Canadian lake country."

Indeed, and perhaps most surprisingly of all, the natural sciences have shared in the general neglect of the Shield. It is a principle of ecology that landform has an equal role with climate in dictating the dispersion of vegetation and animal life. The Shield, which sets up such barriers for people, might be supposed to set up a barrier or two to plants and animals or at least to impose some special conditions. Yet the truth is that among the natural scientists only the geologists have studied the Shield as a geographical unit.

Most of what is known about the flora and fauna of the Shield comes from isolated local studies that have not yet been correlated to give an accurate general picture. Or it comes from broader studies of vegetation types or animal behaviour that ignore the Shield boundaries.

It has to be said, too, that a lot of the research has been done, quite simply, wherever it was easiest to get to. Thus the most exhaustively studied tundra area in Canada is the one around Churchill, Manitoba, at the railhead of the Hudson Bay Railway – and a rich, complex ecology it proves to be. But it is the tundra of the Hudson Bay lowlands, not the tundra of the Shield. In the same way the classic studies of bogs, which were done along the margins of the Shield, are proving to be quite misleading when applied to the muskeg of the central Shield.

There are teasing suggestions that the Shield as a whole does exercise some kind of sorting effect. For example, it is the southern and southwestern edge of the Shield, and not an arbitrary temperature gradient, that conspicuously marks the beginning of the forested region of Canada. And no lizards seem to have gotten on to the Shield, and very few turtles, though there is food for them and the temperatures are within their tolerance.

One other difference has been detected in Shield water. Lakes on the hardrock Shield have been sampled for nutritional values, and these have been compared with lakes in the clay belt of Ontario and in the Hudson Bay lowlands. The lowest values were clearly in the Shield lakes. And, not unexpectedly, the abundance of fish in the lakes could be precisely correlated with the nutrient level.

But otherwise the Shield as a special environment, as an ecological system, has scarcely been considered. For all its importance to the country's ecology, for all its importance to the national development, for all its importance to the culture and image and life-style, the Shield seems to be a Canadian blindspot. Try asking an easterner to mark the boundary of the Shield in Saskatchewan and Alberta, let alone in the high Arctic. Try asking a westerner why Labrador seems such a blank on the map. Ask why so much of Canada is waste space even at temperate latitudes. Ask why, by definition, there cannot be coal or oil in half of Canada, and why the mineral wealth is concentrated in this same half. Ask why the muskeg is there, and the wastes of lichen. Ask why so much of Canada remained literally unmapped for so long.

Two million square miles of ancient hooded rock, stretching from the Atlantic on the east to the Arctic on the far northwest, lapping below the international boundary in the south and disappearing under polar ice in the north; the bulwark of a continent here laid bare, with its proper soil swept off to be the rich cover of the kinder regions; the elemental bedrock, with its hidden riches and its answers to great mysteries: the Canadian Shield.

And – except for the geologists – hardly anyone seems to know it's there.

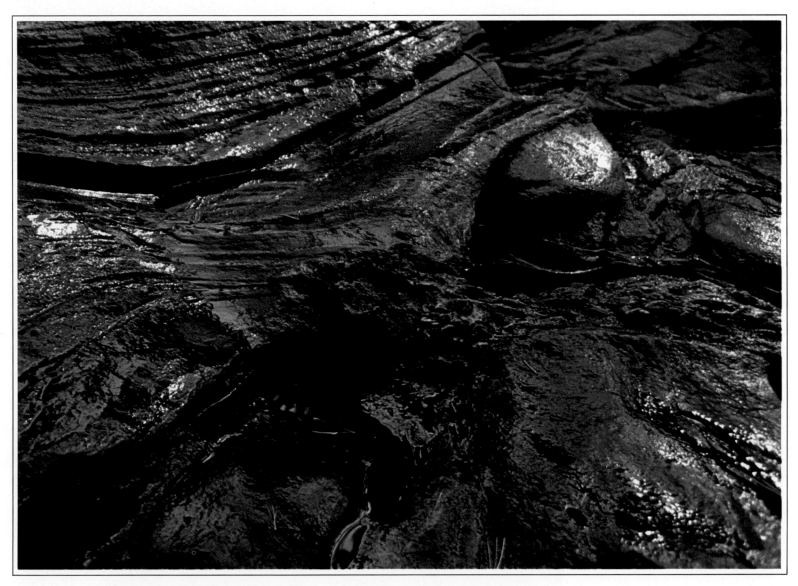

SECRETS IN THE ROCKS

The Canadian Shield: two million square miles of ancient hooded rock, stretching from the Atlantic on the east to the Arctic on the far northwest; the bulwark of a continent here laid bare, with its proper soil swept off; the elemental bedrock, with its hidden riches and its answers to great mysteries.

A fiery beginning

The rocks of the Canadian Shield reveal 85% of earth history and thus contain the evidence for the beginning of the North American continent. Most scientists now think that the earth probably originated from interstellar clouds of gases and dust which slowly condensed and became a molten mass. This mass cooled slowly, until 3½ billion years ago the crust of the earth began to form. Most of what we know about the interior of the earth comes from the study of earthquakes and volcanoes. The crust of the earth has a three mile thick layer of heavy basalt on which sit blocks of lighter granitic rocks—the continental plates, about 40 miles thick. Under this crust is an 1800 mile thick zone of rock called the mantle, beneath which is a central metallic core, the outer half of which is fluid. One of the many theories of continental origin is that as the earth began to cool, it cracked. Gases and magma, which produced lava, escaped through the cracks. The oceans and atmosphere evolved from the gases while the lavas piled up and formed the nucleii of continents. This period of geological history in some areas is called the Keewatin, and is depicted here. The Canadian Shield contains some of the original nucleii of the North American continent.

Ancient volcanic activity and flows of lava in one section of the Shield are represented by the orange and gold colours below.

The core of the Shield

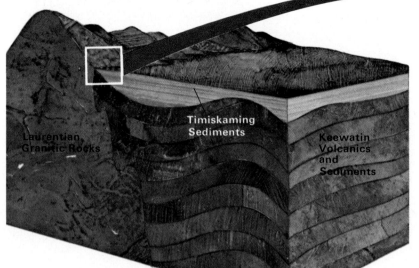

Pre-Algoman

Along the north shore of Lake Superior much of the history of the Shield rocks has been unravelled. The Laurentian granites and Keewatin volcanics are the oldest rocks. Through erosion, the younger Timiskaming sediments accumulated.

The largest single exposure of Precambrian rocks in the world, comprising an area of about two million square miles, is found in the Canadian Shield. The Shield forms the nucleus of the North American continent. While every major continent has a shield nucleus, they are all usually concealed beneath younger cover rocks. The glaciers stripped the Canadian Shield of all preglacial soil and exposed the bare rock to view over much of its extent. Along the outer edges the ancient rocks disappear under a cover of later rocks which have not been stripped away by erosion. The Precambrian era represents such a large portion of the earth's history that geologists are interested in unravelling its twisted and broken record. Much of the mineral wealth of Canada is mined from these rocks, and, in the oldest rocks, geologists find evidence of the condition of the earth's crust and atmosphere when the planet was young. Because the rocks of the Shield have been so deformed, undergoing many mountain-building cycles, volcanic intrusions and erosion, and because fossils are so rare, dating and classifying the rocks is extremely difficult. The Shield itself is divided into provinces, dated according to the time the various mountain-building cycles took place. The oldest province is the Superior and the youngest is the Grenville.

Algoman

Following Timiskaming sedimentation, mountain-building took place accompanied by the granitic intrusions. Many important mineral deposits were formed by these events which are known in geological terms as the Kenoran Revolution.

Precambrian shields are found on every continent throughout the world.

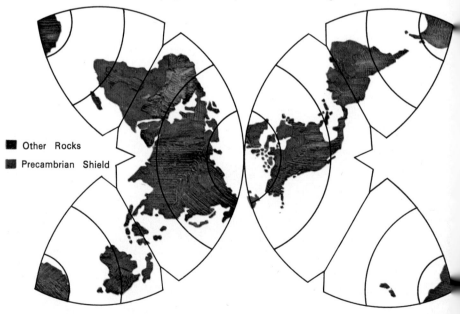

■ Other Rocks

■ Precambrian Shield

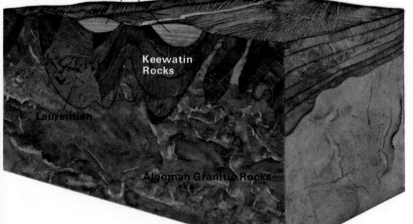

Algoman

A very long period of erosion, several hundred million years, followed by intrusion of the Algoma granite reduced the area to a nearly flat plain. This period of erosion is called the Eparchean interval and was very widespread.

Timiskaming Sediments

Keewatin Rocks

Laurentian

Algoman Granitic Rocks

Animikie

About 1,100,000,000 years ago the area was intruded by diabase sills, named the Logan Sills after Sir William Logan. When eroded, this rock formed such features as the Sleeping Giant and Mount McKay which can be seen on the Shield.

Diabase

Timiskaming Sediments

Proterozoic Sediments

Laurentian

Keewatin

Algoman Granitic Rocks

This cross-section shows the depth of Precambrian basement rocks and the topography. These rocks extend westward beneath the Rocky Mountains.

Plains

Hudson Bay

Atlantic Ocean

Precambrian Rock

The mystery unravelled

Over the last decade or two, intensive geological study of critical areas of the Canadian Shield, structural analyses, and over four hundred age determinations have shown conclusively that the Shield is a composite structure, and not uniform and homogeneous, as was originally believed. The Shield may be divided into structural provinces, each of which contains evidence for major mountain-building episodes comparable with the Appalachian system on the eastern border of this continent and with the Cordilleran system in the west. The differences in the structural trends among the provinces reflects the different directions from which the deforming forces acted during each orogenic episode. In the Grenville Province the trend is northeast; in the Superior Province, east-west; in the Churchill and Ungava Provinces, northeast; and in the Slave Province, north-south. Age determinations reveal that the significant mountain-building events took place at different times in different Provinces. The ages of the oldest rocks in each Province is given below.

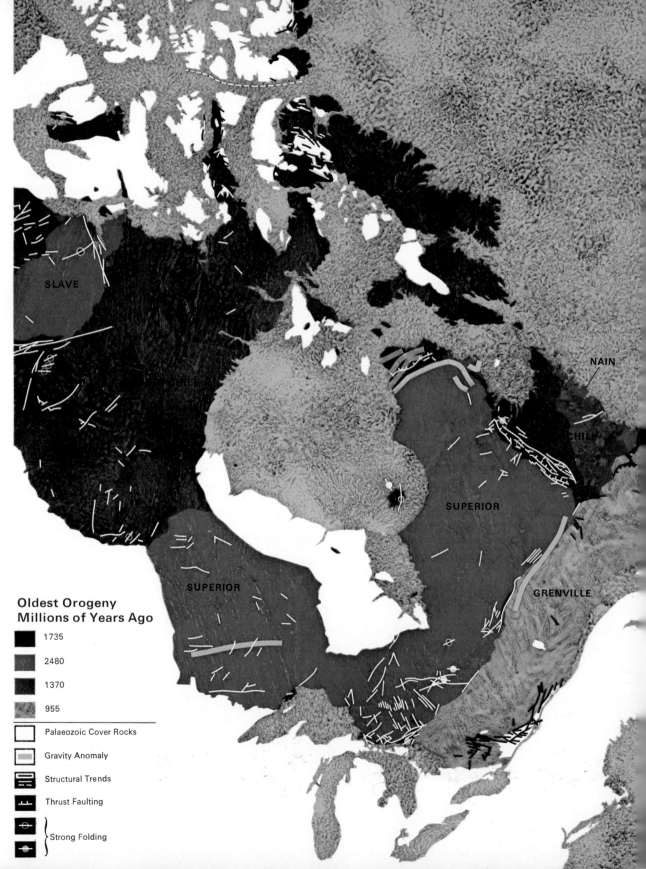

SLAVE

NAIN

CHILL

SUPERIOR

SUPERIOR

GRENVILLE

Oldest Orogeny
Millions of Years Ago

	1735
	2480
	1370
	955
	Palaeozoic Cover Rocks
	Gravity Anomaly
	Structural Trends
	Thrust Faulting
	Strong Folding

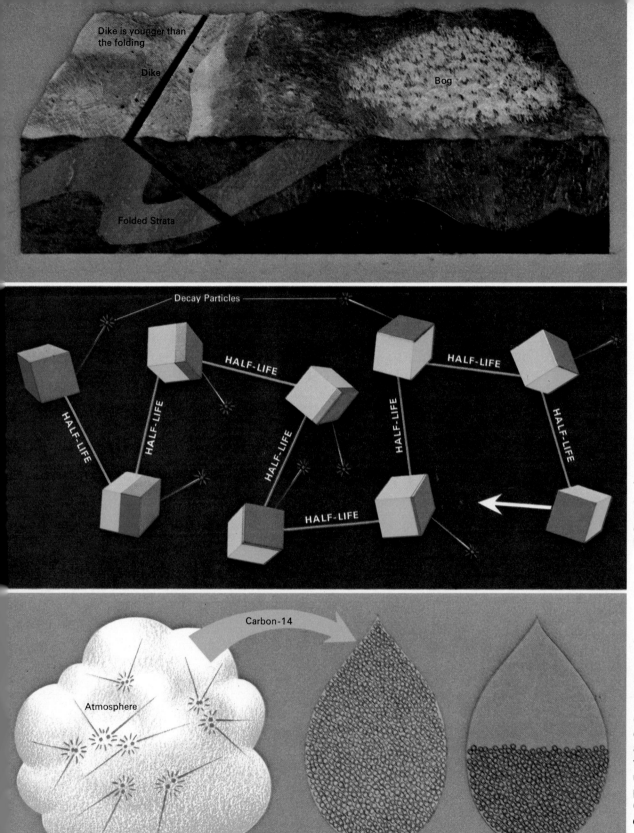

Dike is younger than
the folding

Dike

Folded Strata

Bog

Decay Particles

HALF-LIFE
HALF-LIFE
HALF-LIFE
HALF-LIFE
HALF-LIFE
HALF-LIFE
HALF-LIFE
HALF-LIFE
HALF-LIFE

Carbon-14

Atmosphere

Living Leaf

Dead Leaf

Nature's timeclocks

Relative dating based on simple geological observations is one means of sorting out the mysteries contained in the rocks. A dike intrudes folded strata, therefore the strata is older than the dike. If a dike contains minerals which can be dated radiometrically, the precise age of the intrusion can be determined in years. Materials in bogs that cover the Precambrian rocks are post-glacial in age and can be dated radiometrically.

Radiometric dating allows the geologist to state the time that has elapsed since a rock was formed. The age is based on the radio-active decay of certain elements in the minerals of the rock. The decay of these elements takes place at known rates called the "half-life." Those that decay quickly can be used to date young deposits; those that decay slowly can be used to date old rocks, such as those of the Shield. The method requires a measurement of the quantity of original material, the quantity of the material produced by the decay, and a knowledge of the length of the half-lives.

The Carbon-14 dating process can be used to determine the evolution of the post-glacial environment of the Shield. Since it has a short half-life of 5550 years, by taking samples from the accumulation of organic material in lakes and bogs it can be used to date the deposits associated with the disappearance of glaciers from the Shield. The method depends upon determining the ratio of Carbon-14 present in the deposit to the amount of Carbon-14 that was present in the living organic material.

Nature's accidents

An ore is a high concentration, in a limited area, of elements that are normally found scattered in low concentrations throughout the earth's crust. Ores are the source of the metals used by man. Since man exploits mineral deposits according to his ability to make use of them, an ore body may be looked upon as an accumulation of metal-bearing minerals of sufficient volume to make mining an economically profitable venture. Most metals, with the notable exceptions of iron and aluminium, are statistically rare in nature. The concentrations of all metal-bearing minerals which do occur result from accidents of nature. These accidents are the various geological processes that take place in the earth's crust which created the ore body. Geologists have learned to interpret the signs of likely past activity that could create an ore body of sufficient size to be useful to man. Ores mined from the rocks of the Precambrian Shield are generally associated with igneous processes that took place deep in the earth's crust during Precambrian time. The Precambrian Shield is thus a fertile ground for the exploration of metaliferous ores because of past deep-seated igneous activities and the amount of erosion that has since taken place and brought these ores near the surface of the earth where man can locate and extract them. Three examples of how ores are formed are put in the simplest terms in the diagrams to the right. The complex patterns of geological processes over a huge span of time needed to produce a valuable mineral occurrence can be recognized from the drawings.

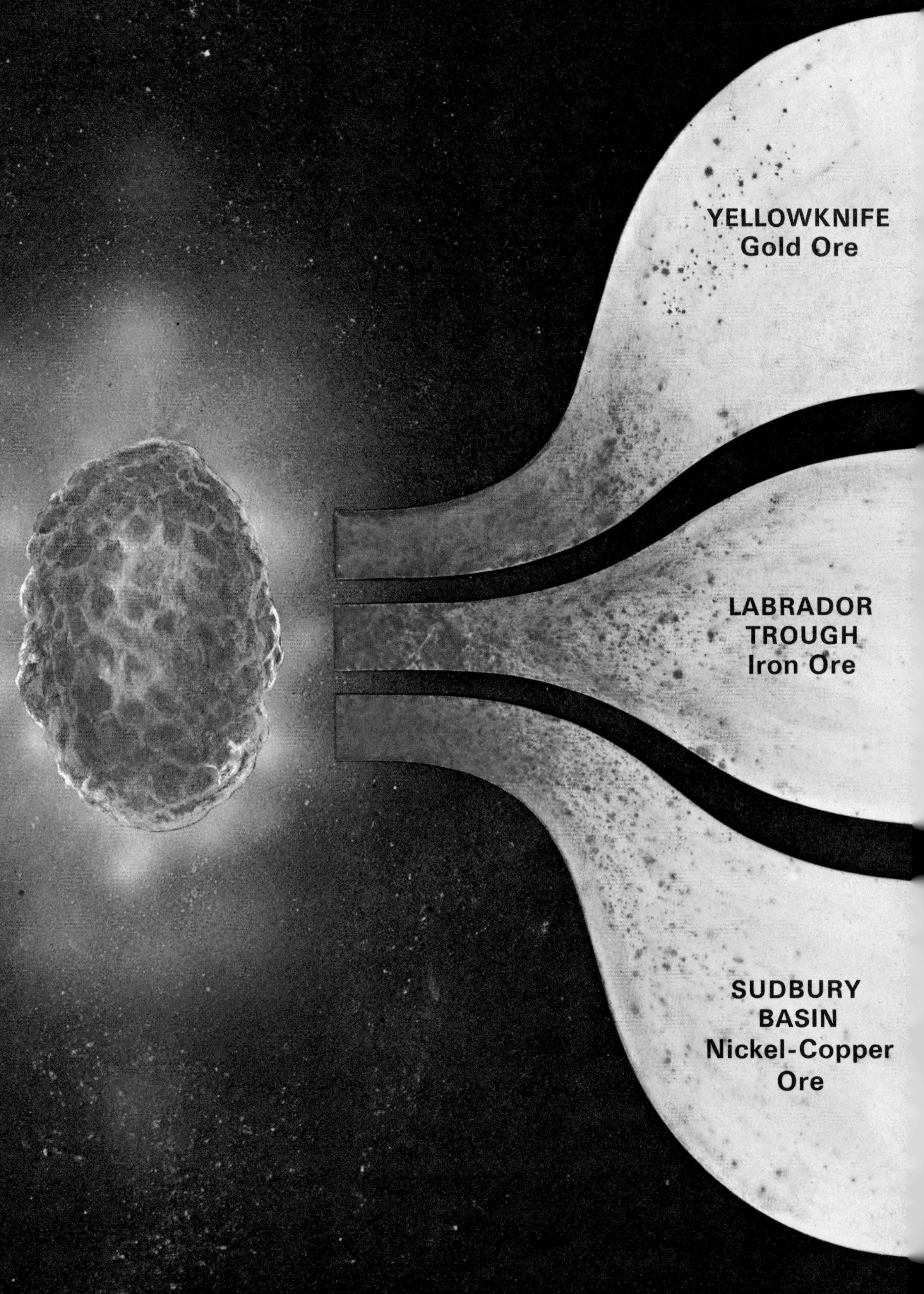

**YELLOWKNIFE
Gold Ore**

**LABRADOR
TROUGH
Iron Ore**

**SUDBURY
BASIN
Nickel-Copper
Ore**

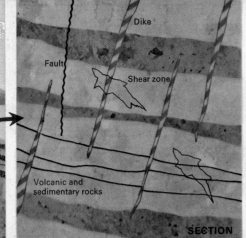
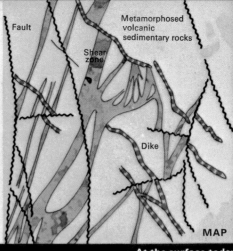

SECTION — In the beginning

Volcanic action · **Sedimentation**

SECTION — At great depth

Dike · Fault · Shear zone · Volcanic and sedimentary rocks

MAP — At the surface today

Fault · Shear zone · Metamorphosed volcanic sedimentary rocks · Dike

An example of the concentration of gold-bearing ore bodies. Large amounts of sedimentary and volcanic rocks accumulated. With deep burial, gold-bearing veins were introduced, mostly in cracks called shear zones. Later, diabase dikes intruded the area. Finally, uplift and erosion exposed the whole complex pattern of rocks found at the earth's surface today.

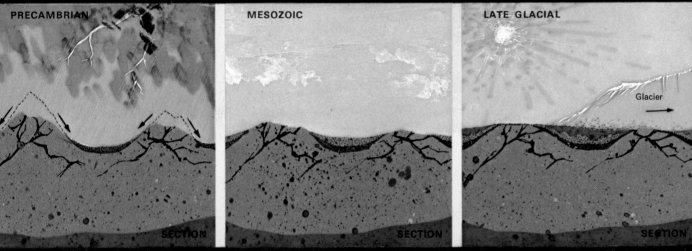

PRECAMBRIAN — **SECTION** — Sedimentation

MESOZOIC — **SECTION** — Weathering

LATE GLACIAL — Glacier — **SECTION** — Glacial withdrawal

An example of how weathering has concentrated iron. Iron-bearing sediments accumulated in large bodies of water in late Precambrian time. Many hundreds of millions of years later, oxidation, ground-water action and other weathering processes produced the iron ore. The large areas of outcrop result from glaciation, which removed pre-glacial soils.

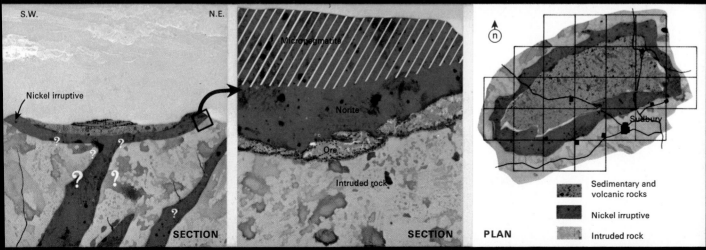

S.W. · N.E. · Nickel irruptive — **SECTION** — The Nickel Irruptive today

Micropegmatite · Norite · Ore · Intruded rock — **SECTION** — Segregation at time of intrusion

n · Sudbury — **PLAN** — The Sudbury Basin today

Sedimentary and volcanic rocks
Nickel irruptive
Intruded rock

An example of the separation of ore minerals from a magma. A large fluid intrusion, called the nickel irruptive, separated into two parts – the light micropegmatite and the heavier norite. The dense copper-nickel sulphide ore minerals occur at the base of the norite and appear to have separated from the norite while both were still in a fluid state.

The Agawa saga

Indian rock paintings, on sheer rock faces in many areas across the Canadian Shield, illustrate important events in Indian history. Most of these sites are today practically inaccessible, but at Agawa Bay, easily reached in Lake Superior Provincial Park, a fascinating interpretation has been made of the red symbols which were painted there hundreds of years ago using iron-stained earth mixed with birds' eggs. A tribesman (left), remembering the savagery of the event, records the story of a war party led across the lake by a warrior named Myeengun. Myeengun is shown on horseback, which confirms his great prestige, for Indians had seen white men riding horses, and the four suns over water tell us that the trip took four days. The saga continues on the Agawa rocks, and a few symbols are reproduced below.
Five canoes made the trip, under the guidance of the spirits which are symbolized by sea serpents, and a safe return is implied by a land turtle. Myeengun claimed the special protection of the mythological *Mishipizhiw*, Ojibwa demi-god of the waters, twice depicted as a great horned animal. Many Indians to this day revere this sinister deity, literally the Great Lynx, and the practice of leaving offerings and prayer-sticks at the foot of certain rock paintings still continues.

Agawa Bay is situated slightly off the Trans-Canada Highway. Road signs indicate short trails leading to the cliff-face.

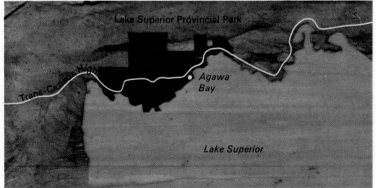

PART TWO / GEOLOGY

4 MYSTERY OF THE SHIELD

Geology as a formal study got started in the late eighteenth century with a retired Scottish doctor named James Hutton, who looked at the sandstone cliffs of his seacoast home, and at the grains of sand being washed ashore and packed down by the waves, and concluded that, given long enough, all the mighty landforms in existence could be accounted for by the accumulation of fragile daily miracles. All the accounting would take was logic and good detective work.

Just so. Starting with Hutton, men learned to sort rocks into the three great orders, sedimentary, igneous and metamorphic, corresponding to the observed processes of sedimentation, as exhibited in the sandstone cliffs; volcanism, as with the great eruptions and lava floods occurring intermittently around the world; and the mutation of rocks under heat and pressure, as with shales involved in mountain-building that were altered to brittle slates and even, sometimes, to contorted mica schists.

According to which sedimentary formations were on top and which were beneath, geologists could deduce the temporal order of events going ever further back in time the lower they went. Even where this order had been deranged by movements of the earth's crust, by faults and folds upwards or downwards, they learned that clues existed to the original succession. The clues were the key fossils. The development of organic life had been orderly, and the stages universal. Thus by studying the fossils in any stratum of rock a geologist could precisely distinguish that rock from strata containing earlier or later fossils; and he could precisely correlate it with rocks containing the same kinds of fossils in formations elsewhere in the world.

The rocks that contained the fossils of the earliest known forms of life were first found and studied in Wales, the land the invading Romans named Cambria. Because of this, all rocks of the same age, everywhere in the world, were called Cambrian, and the same name was used to identify the geological period 500 to 600 million years ago in which this primitive life emerged and the rocks were laid down.

But in certain places in the world – forming, indeed, nine great continental nuclei – there were incredible volumes of rock so old that it seemed to predate this record of life, though microscopic traces of aboriginal organisms have since been found. These wastes of rock seemed, almost always, to be savagely folded and faulted; or deformed as though they had melted and run together; and they were usually so worn by erosion that original relationships were obscured or erased. Since they lacked fossils there were no clues at all to their chronology. They were like a vast continental subconscious. Never mind that the secrets of the first five days of creation were locked in that subconscious: here were depths where logic and detective work seemed helpless. The geologists lumped all such rock together, came to call them Precambrian, or Primitive, or sometimes Azoic, meaning "without life," and dismissed them as a hopeless jumble.

The Canadian Shield is 2,810,000 square miles of just such jumble. Like the other Precambrian areas it has, by definition, no clear fossil clues. As a corollary, Precambrian rock cannot yield coal, oil, natural gas, or indeed any other fossil fuel. And it is so disordered and deformed that it has been described as "scar tissue."

Even with modern techniques the full sequence of events in their formation can't be untangled. Parts of the Shield are still virtually unknown and unexplored. Consequently no neat, comfortable narrative of the origin of the Shield and its development is possible. It may never be.

But what can be told is Part One of an engrossing detective story.

For the geologists finally came to the Shield and step by step the Shield began yielding up secrets. James Hutton was right, up to a point: logic and stubborn detective work can do a lot. Step by step, some of its traits were recognized. Parts of its history were decoded. Structural patterns were pieced together. Strangely enough, the findings served only to increase the mysteries, or create even larger ones. The Shield offered anomalies and difficulties that no existing theories seemed able to account for; it still does. But now a threshold has been reached.

Tuzo Wilson, the Canadian earth scientist, has pointed out that so far man understands pathetically little about the fundamental processes of his own planet. As long as this is so he can neither interpret its present condition nor correctly reconstruct its past. But Wilson has also suggested that we are on the brink of a revolution in geophysical understanding comparable to the revolution in physics worked by quantum mechanics or the revolution in biology worked by Darwin's theories.

This is where the story has got so far. This is the context in which the Canadian Shield is being studied today – and suddenly everything about it has turned dramatic and suggestive. The clues are beginning to make sense. For the real riddles of the Shield are now clearly the riddles of the planet earth itself.

Man knows or can guess some things about the earth. For example, he knows it is a second-class planet orbiting a middle-aged third rate star moving randomly among other stars in the outer suburbs of a rather large spiral galaxy, the Milky Way, that cartwheels sluggishly every two hundred million years, in a universe whose centre or edge cannot be perceived.

He guesses, from various sorts of evidence, that the solar system came into being some four and a half billion years ago. There are a number of theories about this birth. The most popular theory at the moment is that the earth began as a clotting of ordinary cosmic dust, at room temperature so to speak, but then grew so hot through compression and internal nuclear activity that it melted for a while. There seems to be agreement, certainly, that the earth was molten at an early stage, and that the first crust didn't form till as many as a billion years had gone by.

Man knows that the earth is a thermal machine, and a giant magnet, and that it is very, very slightly egg-shaped rather than completely round. Seismic evidence indicates that it is layered with a thin brittle crust, a denser intermediate zone that behaves in some respects like Silly Putty, and a core that may be pure nickel-iron.

He knows that the earth is denser than any other planet in the solar system – so dense, in fact, that the only explanation seems to be the presence of uncommon amounts of the heavy metals. This is why he has guessed that the core is nickel-iron.

He knows it is the only planet with significant amounts of free oxygen, the product, but also the precondition of life, and of free liquid water. Indeed there is so much water that the earth's present surface is really oceanic rather than continental. Water covers three-quarters of the globe. If the continents were levelled out, water would cover all of it to a depth of a mile and a half. He knows earth is the only planet whose surface is divided into continents and oceans.

What man doesn't know is the rule, the working principle, by which his planet evolved from a primal dustball to the multiform and hospitable world he knows. He really doesn't see why it shouldn't be as flinty and sterile a sphere as the Moon or Mars.

Or, to go a step further: granted the presence of the water envelope, man doesn't, simply doesn't, know why any dry land should rise clear of it. Nothing demonstrates more clearly than the presence and persistence of continents that there has to be a working principle.

For we know of no terrestrial process more inexorable than erosion. Second by second, day by day, eon by eon, wind and frost, rust and chemical rot, rains and river-torrents tear down and weather away the land. The rate of erosion can be estimated. So can the volume of continental material. Given the length of geological time, the continents should long since have been washed away like so many sand castles, and their sediments distributed over the ocean floor in a layer averaging, it has been calculated, some seven or eight miles thick.

Instead, the land persists – standing an average of three miles above the ocean floors indicating that some processes were at work to keep restoring or rebuilding them.

For a long time it seemed satisfactory to believe that the earth was cooling from the molten state; that as it did so the crust had to wrinkle and ruck up into folds to accommodate the shrinking core; and that these folds, rising above sea level, formed the continents. But this agreeably simple notion won't do. For one thing, far from cooling off the earth may actually be warming up very, very slightly. For another thing, the earth has stretch marks as well as wrinkles: rift valleys and great zones of fracture that are scars of tension, rather than of compression and shrinkage.

But most importantly, for this account to be true the continents and ocean floors need to be a single continuous skin with the lowlands cradling the seas and the uplands rising clear. They are not. It is a recent and startling discovery and one that has profoundly shaken the geological world. The ocean floors and the continents are as different as mouth-lining is from ordinary skin.

The ocean floors contain no known ore-bodies. The ocean floors are marked by great submarine ridge-systems, as mighty as the continental mountain ranges, but much simpler in structure. The oldest fossils yet found in the ocean floors, in some ten thousand core samples, date from no further back than the age of the dinosaurs.

And the ocean floors are made of a dense, dark basaltic rock, heavy with silicates of magnesium and iron. Indeed, this same basaltic rock seems to encase the globe, extending even under the continents – and sagging into the mantle under their weight. The average thickness of this layer is about five miles. In it, the continents are no more than alien blisters and patches.

The material of the continents is quite different from that of the ocean floors. Though rocks of many kinds occur on land including basaltic rock in volcanic regions, their average composition is quite distinct from that of basalt. Instead it approximates that of a rock called granodiorite, which is intermediate between basalt and granite. Whereas basalt is rich in magnesium and iron, granite is rich in aluminum, and super-rich in silica. Whereas basalt is dense and dark, granite is light in colour and light in weight. True granite is a sort of logical extreme: the lightest fraction that would surface if basalt and granite were melted and allowed to differentiate by gravity. It does not occur at all in the ocean basins; indeed, in spite of popular belief, true granite is a comparatively rare rock even on land. But the average continental building-stuff is far enough along the scale towards this archetype to warrant the description granitic. The continents, that is to say, are islands of impure granitic scum that have accumulated on the surface of the basalt.

Continents have a random assortment of arbitrary outlines and are mostly clustered in the northern hemisphere, the so-called "land hemisphere," with their tails tapering away south. These northern continents ring an ocean basin that occupies the polar position. In the southern hemisphere the continent of Antarctica occupies the corresponding polar position and is ringed by seas.

Continents are infinitely more complex in structure than ocean floors. They are zoned into Shield areas, fringing sedimentary plains, and coastal mountain ranges. These mountain systems are active and persist from one continent to the next; they link, in turn, to long festoons of offshore volcanic island-chains, thus completing a continuous baseball-seam pattern of global disturbance.

Continents contain ore-bodies, and instead of the mere five miles of the basaltic ocean floor layer are, on average, twenty-two miles thick. Rock in the Shield areas shows that continents are more than twenty times older than the ocean floors. By what mechanism do the continents persist? Where did they come from? How did they begin?

Even when the earth seemed a simple place, and continents only natural, it was clear that Shield areas held the answer to some of these great mysteries. These rigid uplands of ancient rock, which seem to have stood aloof from all geological events save quiet erosion since before life began, were the only surviving record of the first four-fifths of earth's history. And the mysteries of origin have always teased and fascinated men.

James Hutton had insisted that the present was the key to the past. If only a way could be found to untangle the sequence of Precambrian rocks; if only what had been laid down later could be distinguished from what had been laid down earlier, and earlier still, and so back and back and back in time; it might ultimately be possible to arrive at the first, the original, crust of the earth. And what might that not tell about the nature of the planet?

Enter the detectives.

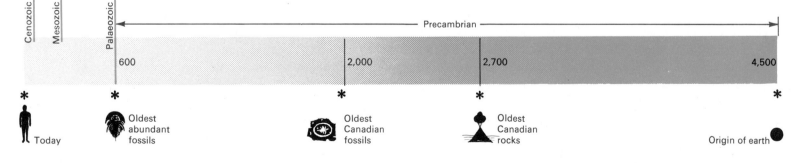

✳ Ages in millions of years

5 EARLY INVESTIGATIONS

The first Canadian Shield investigator was there because he hadn't much choice. In 1842 the government of the recently united Upper and Lower Canada set up a Geological Survey, and gave it a grant of £1500 sterling to map the two provinces and take inventory of their natural resources. The first director of the Survey was William Logan, a Scots bachelor, who had spent the ten years prior to his appointment studying the coalfields in Wales. As soon as he received his appointment, Logan naturally went off looking for coal. He would have done better among the younger rocks of the Maritimes, but here in the United Province of Canada, of course, he found no coal. Instead, what he found was an upland waste of Precambrian rock. So, as Director of the Survey, that was what Logan studied.

It must have seemed a thankless labour. For one thing, Logan and his colleagues were working in the geological dark. The primitive rocks had been little studied elsewhere in the world, so there was virtually no background of Precambrian lore. The term "shield," and the concept it implied of an extensive stable core to every continent, had yet to be coined: the Austrian geologist Eduard Suess invented it in 1892.

The incredible extent in time and area of the rocks wasn't even guessed at. There was just this area in Quebec and Ontario called the Laurentian Plateau. The first geological map of Canada, published in 1864, showed no more than a belt of primitive rocks along the north shore of the Saint Lawrence to the Labrador coast, and a second belt stretching northwest from Ottawa to Lake Huron and proceeding along the north shore of Huron and Superior into eastern Manitoba. North of these belts the map was blank. Indeed Canada was to be well into the twentieth century before the outline of the Shield was completed to include the Precambrian in the high Arctic. And even as recently as 1940 it was estimated that ninety per cent of the Shield was unknown country, crossed by only a few lines of exploration, and seen by only a few people.

Adding to the difficulties was the terrain itself – trackless, craggy, interrupted by scarp and swamp and muskeg, often thickly forested. The surveyors travelled by canoe, by dog team, or on foot. As they pushed along they patiently made notes on each outcrop and tried to link it to the next in order to outline important masses of rock. They were beset by mosquitoes and black flies. The ancient, compacted rock was hard enough to wear out, in one summer, boots that had withstood years of mountaineering in Europe. And the season for field work was very short. Even today, one Precambrian geologist says firmly, "I know of no science where a researcher is beset by more difficulties than a geologist field-mapping in the Canadian Shield."

None of this is to speak of the difficulties of the geology itself. Only ten per cent of the rocks on the Shield actually outcrop: the rest are hidden under thin soil, or dense bush, or muskeg. But even when the outcrops can be linked and separate masses distinguished, the structures are nightmarishly complex: great thicknesses of two or three kinds of rocks, implying two or three different origins, may be pushed up together into loose pleats, or into folds that fall back on themselves like toothpaste; then stood on end or overturned completely; and then eroded so that the softer and more vulnerable members have disappeared.

Logan himself, in his monumental report on the Geology of Canada in 1863, spelled out the difficulties for his employers and added somewhat defensively, "A labour such as this . . . must necessarily require much time."

But Logan and his colleagues were nothing if not stubborn. One of them, Albert Low, was sent on a joint federal-provincial survey to the Lake Mistassini area in 1884. Along in January he got into a jurisdictional dispute with the leader of the Quebec half of the party, put on his snowshoes, and hiked out to get a ruling from his superiors in Ottawa, just under four hundred miles away. After winning full command of the expedition he walked the four hundred miles back, in time to start the summer's operations.

So in time these early surveyors sorted out several main kinds of rock occurrence, and the theoretical order in which they had been laid down. Time has proved them not altogether right about the order, but the work was fundamental all the same. These were the first major distinctions to be recognized in Precambrian rock, and even today the Shield as a whole can be crudely but rewardingly mapped by using them. They are worth understanding in some detail, for each was to take on more and more meaning as time went by.

The first rock type to be distinguished was what might be called the country rock of the Shield – a generalized ground-mass that seemed to have some of the characteristics of granite but a quite different and rather queer texture. Geologists call it gneiss (pronounced *nice*) or banded gneiss. The word gneiss is of Slavonic origin and means rotted or decomposed: it has been borrowed as the generic term to signify an altered rock in which the constituent minerals have segregated themselves and withdrawn into collateral bands and ribbons. Layers of granular minerals alternate with each other, or with layers of fibrous or platey minerals such as mica, so that the rock appears striped. The process is a metamorphosis: something that happens to many kinds of rock under severe extremes of heat and pressure. If the heat and pressure have been less, the effect is less clearly marked, and the rock will usually split open fairly easily along the fibrous layer. In this case it is called a schist, from the Greek *schistos*, meaning split. But true gneiss is so dense and compacted that it can bounce a geological hammer.

It has been customary to describe the Shield gneisses as granitic gneisses. Actually, gneisses cover a wide range of compositions and indeed, if the Shield gneisses are averaged chemically, the result is identical to the average continental building material. They are, that is to say, granodioritic: intermediate between the basic oceanic rock and true granite. But while the familiar granite of tombstones and public buildings is as plumply grained as salami, gneiss is visibly dishevelled. It is sometimes choked with swollen, massive crystals of one of its minerals, while the others dwindle to mere pinstripes. The bands can be broad and regular, or they can grade into inane scribbles. In places there may be whorls of granite, like eddies in a stream. It is hard to avoid images of a sluggish, streaky, half-stirred porridge flooding the land and congealing.

Logan himself studied the gneisses and rightly concluded that though they were often granitic in composition and recurrently graded into granitic texture they were something other than granite. But he misread the stripes and bands as being the traces of an original sedimentary layering rather than an effect of actual migration of minerals under heat and pressure. Because of this he decided that the rocks were metamorphosed sediments, perhaps in part of special primitive types not duplicated later in geological history. In fact he thought it possible that these very sedi-

ments had been erosion products – all that remained – of the original crust. He called them the Fundamental Gneiss. And he concluded, of course, that the Fundamental Gneiss underlay all the other rocks.

He went on to distinguish the rock systems that seemed to him to lie above the Fundamental Gneiss.

The first system consisted of great volumes of metamorphosed volcanic products, with lesser amounts of metamorphosed sediments, called metasediments, interfingered or folded in. Only eons of volcanic activity interspersed with periods of marine flooding and quiet erosion could have produced them. There had, then, been huge volcanic piles in the Shield in ancient times.

These volcanics seemed to occur in great welts in the universal gneiss, some a hundred miles or more long and as much as eight miles thick. The lavas obviously had varied chemical compositions, but many of them seemed to be basalts, like those of the ocean floors, or else the allied andesites which also come heavy and dark with iron and rich with magnesium from deep in the earth. They weigh heavy in the hand, like cinder or slag, and have the dense, fine texture imposed by instant crystallization.

But minerals containing iron and magnesium are unstable. Under even mild metamorphosis, basalts and andesites alter readily to various secondary combinations. The most common products are the chlorites, soft, tough minerals akin to mica though not so flexible. And chlorites are green. So the metamorphosed Shield volcanics have a noticeable and characteristic green cast, and are commonly known as greenstones. The greenstones occur in the same great welts in many places in the Shield, and gold and other precious metals seem to be associated with them.

The second kind of assembly that Logan thought directly to overlie the Fundamental Gneiss was almost the exact reverse of a greenstone belt with its sparse lacing of metasediments. This was a massive system of metasediments with a few associated volcanics, plus intruded granites.

Logan found this assembly to the south of his band of greenstones and traced it, in a broad general swathe, from the shores of Georgian Bay eastward through Ontario to somewhere beyond the borders of Quebec. It was patchy, and interrupted by

THE FIRST SETTLERS

The colonizing lichens are so called because they are often the first plants to settle and grow on the surface of bare rocks. They can also flourish under water and on mountain-tops, existing, in fact, from tropics to tundra.

Living together

Lichens are, in effect, perennial plants of double ancestry, for, while they are commonly treated as single plant species and classified into genera, they are born of an uniquely intimate association between an alga and a fungus. Neither of the component plants alone possesses any of the characteristics shown by the two in combination, and their mutually beneficial association is called symbiosis. In the lichen, the fungus alone is capable of fruiting, although the algal cells do increase and multiply. At the same time, the algae carry on photosynthesis, and thereby manufacture the lichen's food. Lichens blanket the rocks with a variety of colourful designs.

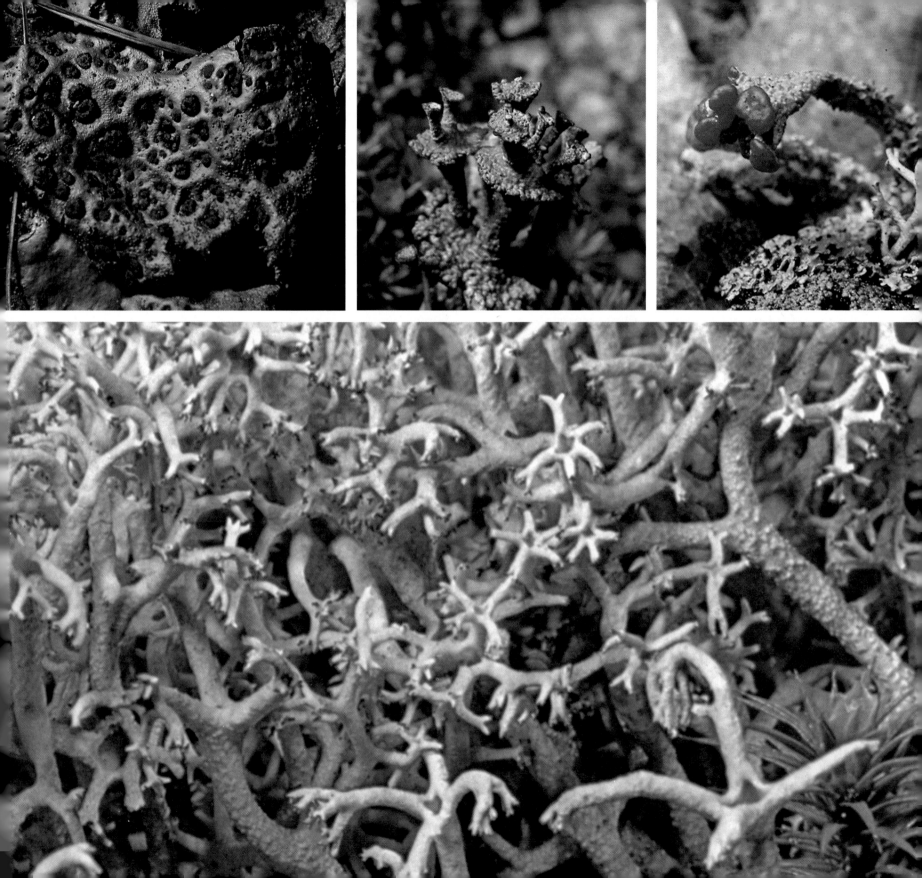

gneisses, but the outcrops could be linked because the metasediments themselves were unmistakable. They had a kind of Aladdin's Cave glamour. There were quartz-mica schists (altered shales) as ancient and gnarled as oyster shells, that twisted apart along congested planes of green-gold mica flakes. There were other schists studded with garnets, or with blades of milky-blue kyanite. There were pastel quartzites (altered sandstones) with a caked coarse glitter. One of them, green with stray chrome, was the rare algoma jade used by jewellers. And above all, there were true marbles (altered limestones and dolomites) white as sugar, or icing-pink, or sherbet-green.

Logan and his colleagues worked mainly on the margins of the Shield in Ontario and Quebec. (Even today this section is the only really well-studied part of it.) Unfortunately time was to prove that this great southern band of glittering metasediments was far from typical. But accounting for it – and understanding the crucial association of copious metasediments with interfingered volcanics and intrusive granites – would be vital to understanding the Shield. Time was also to prove that Logan's Fundamental Gneiss was far from being of uniform age, that it could by no means be dismissed as a universal basement layer, and that it occurred in staggering, nearly incredible, volumes.

Four-fifths of the rock of the Shield – a million and a half square miles in area and no one knows how many miles in depth – would prove to be gneiss. How to account for it was to become one of the consuming problems of the Shield – and of the origin of continents.

In these endless wastes of enigmatic rock occurred the scattered pods and welts of greenstones. These, too, were going to have to be accounted for: the remnants of mighty volcanic piles persisting in the floods of gneiss that seemed to have engulfed and obliterated so much else.

The gneisses were also interrupted by outcrops of the great regional belt of rocks dominated by the glittering anomalous metasediments. And though nothing quite like these particular metasediments could be found anywhere else, the recurrent association of thick altered sediments with interlaced volcanics and intruded granites was to puzzle geologists for decades.

Logan and his colleagues made one other working distinction among Shield rocks. It amounted to the first subdivision of Precambrian time. They assigned the Fundamental Gneiss, the greenstones and certain other assemblies of rock that seemed closely associated with them to the Archaean (meaning "very ancient") or earlier part of the history of the Shield. The rest of the rocks, including the brilliant band of metasediments, they assigned to the latter part, which came to be known as the Proterozoic (meaning "time of earlier life") era of the Precambrian. The distinction still has real validity: many Proterozoic forma-

Under perfect conditions, minerals occur in regular geometric forms, like those below, called crystals. These forms are related to the atomic structure of the mineral and may be used to identify it. Perfect crystals are rare, but even a fragment will yield basic data to the expert.

For those interested in rocks and minerals, rock collecting paves the way for more serious study. There are over 2,000 mineral species, but many thousands of different kinds of rocks. The equipment used on an amateur rock collecting trip can be simple: notebook and labels for identification, pick, hammer and chisel, magnifying glass, and a satchel for carrying back samples.

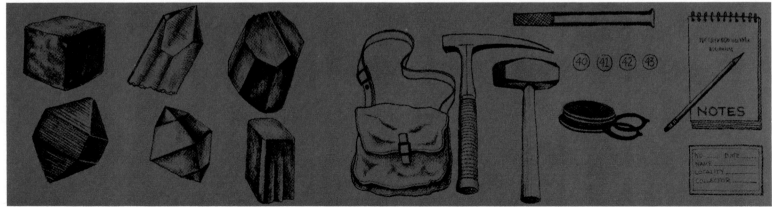

tions have a different and broader structural style. And Proterozoic formations have been found to contain kinds of rocks not present earlier, as though there had been some adjustment in earth chemistry.

The Geological Survey was, of course, a branch of the civil service and it had the government's work to do. Surveying and mapping occupied most of the time in the field in the early days. Indeed, in any other country the men of the Survey would long since have been hailed as the heroic explorers they were.

But the public now had a new requirement of the Survey. In 1882 a CPR crew was engaged in cutting the railway line through the Shield. One day, the story goes, at a point on the main line about three miles northwest of what is now Sudbury, a blacksmith named Tom Flanagan saw a rusty stain on the face of their excavation. He recognized the stain, called "gossan" as the sign of nickel-copper sulphides rotting at an exposed surface.

Jesuit missionaries had heard about the copper of Lake Superior as early as 1636. Indeed, even before the coming of the white man, the Indians had known that the Shield held great mineral treasure. But for two and a half centuries, everyone who tried to get it out went broke.

The Sudbury strike, though, was not only a big one: it was on the railway. With transportation, the riches could be brought out to market. In the same way, the building of the Ontario Northland Railway brought the great silver discoveries at Cobalt in 1903-4.

Prospectors spreading out from the Cobalt field found gold at Porcupine and Kirkland Lake, and soon mines were springing up like mushrooms in all the more accessible parts of the Shield. There was gold, though not always in workable quantities, almost everywhere. And there was iron at Michipicoten and at Knob Lake and Steep Rock. There was lead and zinc, and platinum and molybdenum and asbestos. There was cobalt and cadmium; selenium and tellurium and titanium; sulphur and tungsten and pitchblende and kaolin and graphite and the rare earths and a host of other valuable and ornamental minerals. Even diamonds have been found – in glacial drift in Wisconsin that came from the Shield – though men are still unsuccessfully trying to back-track to the mother lode.

For most of the fifty years following the Sudbury find, the Survey was called on to devote itself to untangling the formations in all the various mining districts. The idea was to be able to follow the mineral occurrences beyond the original strike. A latterday geologist has called it "postage-stamp work." It was. But out of just such work, together with the geological notes of the mappers, an invaluable dossier on the Shield would eventually be built up. And it was, even thus localized and specific, a formidable task. It is worth looking at an example.

Mineral identification often requires expensive laboratory equipment, and detailed chemical and physical tests which can be made only by experts. However, several simple physical tests may be learned by the amateur. Magnetism (1) occurs in a few minerals; on a field trip, an ultra-violet lamp can be used to detect fluorescent minerals (2); a geiger counter (3) is used to locate radio-active minerals; small amounts of mineral introduced into a flame (4) will colour the flame, depending on the metal present; other tests (5) may involve heating a powdered mineral to detect the nature of the fumes produced or the deposit which has accumulated on the side of the test tube.

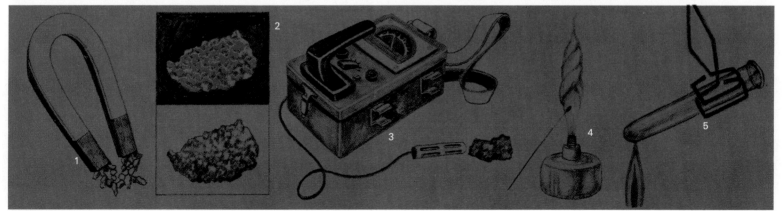

6 ROCK LAID BARE

The richest nickel mines in the world are at Sudbury, Ontario – and there is even more copper than nickel, though the fact is seldom advertised. Copper had been noticed in the district as early as 1856 but it aroused little interest until the completion of the CPR in 1885 made transport of the ore practical.

If you come into Sudbury by air, you can see quite clearly a low ring of hills with a flat-lying basin in the centre. The hills are eroded nubs of dark granular rock and they are the location of the main ore deposits. Actually the ring is warped into an oval, with its long axis pointing northeastward. The oval is about thirty-seven miles long and about fifteen miles across.

A survey geologist named Robert Bell was the first to outline, in 1890, the "distinct geological basin" as the central feature of the rich new mining area, and to recognize it as being of peculiar interest. Not many ring-shaped features occur in nature. Since that time it has been as intensively studied as any Precambrian region in the world, not just at the surface but underground through miles of mine workings. (The ore-bearing hills vary from one to three miles in depth.) Yet even today there is hot dispute about every theory the geologists have advanced to account for it.

There is a lot to be accounted for. The basin inside the ring of hills contains a most extraordinary succession of rocks. At the base of the succession is a zone of shattered quartzite (altered sandstone). It looks like rock that has been reconsolidated from the rubble of a giant wrecking-ball: all broken, blocky slabs and bits caked together with rock dust.

Above this is what is known as the Onaping formation. It is a massive stratum of dense flinty dark-purple-to-brown rock which is very tough. It seems to have been consolidated from volcanic ash and debris. But incorporated in this ground-mass are fragments of fused-looking but recognizable granite, gneiss and metasediments that seem to have been blasted from the country rock outside the basin. They range in size from minute particles to giant blocks. The whole has been cemented into a single mass that must originally have been nearly a mile thick, and it is capped by a thin veneer of shallow-water sediments – limestone and chert – that clearly belong to the same time sequence. The top layer of the succession consists of late shales that have been altered to slates and, above, thick ordinary sandstone.

A tale of explosion and violence and volcanic eruption, followed in due course by quiet underwater sedimentation? Perhaps. But the first great Sudbury puzzle is that this remarkable series of rocks lacks any parallel outside the basin. Quite simply, the country rock offers no duplicates for the shattered zone of quartzite at the base, or for the ordinary sediments on top. As for the Onaping formation: no volcanic source for it can be found in the neighbourhood at all. There are no vents. The necessary underground feeder systems are missing. Furthermore, there are no corresponding deposits of ash outside the basin, no mighty thicknesses of lava where they ought to be. It is almost as though the basin and its contents had been transported from elsewhere and set down in alien terrain.

If so, it was certainly set down with uncanny precision in a most interesting spot. That is the second great Sudbury puzzle. For the basin is right at a geological crossroads. To the north lie wastes of the familiar Shield gneisses and greenstones. To the south and west lies a region of metasediments, with minor volcanics and intruded granites, in the association that the early Surveyors had come to regard as typical and significant. The whole region is intensely folded and faulted. To the southeast lies the beginning of that great swathe of rocks, stretching off towards the Atlantic, that is distinguished by the peculiar glittering metasediments. Indeed the Sudbury basin lies right beside the disturbed boundary zone, known as the Grenville Front, that marks the junction of these rocks with the gneisses to the north.

Furthermore the basin also lies right on the intersection of two major fault systems, one striking approximately north-south and the other east-west. The east-west system, called the Murray Fault System, has been traced over a hundred miles from east of Sudbury to west of Blind River. Displacement along the fault has certainly been as much as a mile, and geologists estimate that it must have been active on and off for over a billion years.

Cutting off the anomalous little basin from this panorama of clash and disturbance is the encircling collar of hills, usually called "the nickel irruptive." It is the third great Sudbury puzzle. One mystery, of course, is its shape: so far as is known, nothing quite like this closed circle of intruded rock exists anywhere else in the world. And then there is its composition. The hills are igneous, which is to say their rock has once been molten deep in the earth but has made its way upward to a point in the crust where it could cool slowly and crystallize. But it is of two kinds: the outer part of the ring is dense, dark basic rock, like basalt in composition; the inner part is light and granitic. The ore occurs around the outer edges of the intrusive in the footwall rocks. It occurs in the form of bodies of almost pure copper and nickel iron sulphides; as veins and stringers of sulphides; and as a flush of minerals all through the containing rock. That is the circumstantial evidence. What have the investigators made of it?

One theory, for example, starts with the Onaping formation and its overlying sediments already in place, not only on the future site of the basin but extending to the south as well, in a continuous layer. This theory rests on the belief that the whole layer lay on an eroded surface of Shield gneiss, and that the contact between the two different rock types constituted a horizontal plane of weakness. Thus, when the molten rock that was to become the irruptive welled up from the depths and reached this contact-horizon, it was able to spread out into a sheet separating the two. Such a horizontal sheet is called a sill.

Then some mysterious kind of structural squeeze in the crust acted to grip the sill into a cup shape whose edges–the irruptive– cut off the rocks inside from the rocks outside. Because the rocks inside the basin were protected, this theory goes, they remained relatively undisturbed and unaltered. The comparable rocks outside to the south, on the other hand, were later subjected to heat and pressure that altered them beyond recognition.

A variation of this theory turns a little more directly towards explaining the shape of the basin and irruptive. It suggests that, sometime after the underground reservoir of molten rock had emptied itself upwards into the sill, the added weight overhead caused it to collapse and fall in on itself dragging the sill into a tilted circle of upthrust slabs around an enclosed basin. From then on, in the same way, the rocks in the basin were protected from any violent events outside to the south.

Both these views rest on a difficult – and, to some, quite unacceptable – chemical correlation of the basin rocks with the

The complex patterns in the picture at the right result from igneous intrusions penetrating through light coloured country rock.

tortured metasediments and metavolcanics to the south.

There is a third theory. It is considerably more elaborate and colourful, for, as a product of many different lines of investigation, it tries to account for almost all the circumstantial evidence. But it, too, assumes an unknown.

The unknown is a large depression that needs already to have existed on the site of the Sudbury basin before any recognizable geological event took place. There is no attempt to explain the origin of the depression nor why its perimeter should mark a line of weakness in the rocks, but both are necessary to the theory.

It starts, then, with the depression and its weakened rim. Everywhere there is shallow sea. Below in the crust is a great chamber of molten rock, under pressure. It wells up, probing for weak spots. Unerringly, it finds the ring-shaped line of weakness, fractures it, and bursts through to the surface to build a ring of high volcanic cones in the sea. The sea is a necessary part of the picture, for it explains the sediments both inside and outside the basin and it also accounts for "pillow lavas" that have been found among the volcanics outside: only lavas deposited underwater chill quickly enough to form these characteristic overlapping blurts of rock. The volcanoes built up for a long time from the sea floor, then, their flanks criss-crossed by fissures: and for a long time the lava welled and poured outward from the fissures into the surrounding sea.

Later, though, the ring of volcanoes burst like Vesuvius into violent eruption. Inside the basin, great flowing, effervescing avalanches of gas-charged lava poured down headlong from all sides, carrying with them shattered fragments of the exploding cones. Since the Onaping formation has no perceptible layering, the assumption is that the deposit was built up to its thickness of nearly a mile with tremendous speed – probably in the space of only a few years. (Paricutin Volcano, in Mexico, started as a spurt of grey dust from a crack that opened in a cornfield in February, 1943; by 1946 it had grown a cone 1500′ high.)

The sudden accumulation of more than three hundred cubic miles of volcanic debris within the little Sudbury basin would involve rapid drainage of the underlying chambers of molten rock. This presumably caused the floor of the basin to subside still farther. Meanwhile, outside the basin, normal sediments from the eroding volcano cones had joined the lavas in the sea. And,

inside the basin, hot springs had arisen, producing conditions in which limestones and cherts could be laid down. Later still, shallow stagnant water in the basin favoured the deposition of the clays and sand that were to become the slate and sandstone.

Thus far in the story, most of the contents of the basin have been accounted for, as well as a few of the puzzling features, such as pillow lavas, to be found outside. But the mysterious vanishing volcanoes, the arrival of the twinned nickel irruptive, and the contradictions in the surrounding terrain remain to be explained.

So, it is next suggested, molten rock from the depths in time filled an underground chamber slightly south of the basin's south rim. Perhaps this happened when the region to the southwest was being so severely folded and faulted. In any case, before it welled up to where it could solidify, the molten rock separated by gravity into a heavier basaltic reservoir and a lighter granitic one. The basaltic rock found its way upwards first, along the feeder pipes and fissures and fractures of the ancient volcanic ring. Then the granitic fraction was introduced along the same path, as an inner ring. The emplacement has been dated at about one and three-quarter billion years ago, in the early Proterozoic part of the Precambrian. The two intrusions together wiped out or buried all traces of the ancient volcanic vents. Later still, during some period of crustal stress, the minerals in the form of sulphurous liquids and gases were injected along the same vulnerable path as the irruptive itself. And the basin's pivotal location at a geological intersection? No one has the answer. One authority has said: "Like vultures, all the problems of Precambrian geology come home to roost at Sudbury."

All that can be said is that the history of the gneisses to the north in relation to the basin remains an enigma. A contemporary link seems likely between the irruptive emplacement and the intense folding and alteration of the region to the southwest. And as for the great linear tract of rocks stretching off from the Grenville Front towards the Atlantic: some great crustal convulsion from the south caught it up later, squeezing and folding it, deforming and recrystallizing its rocks, creating the strange glittering metasediments that Logan studied. The same stresses warped the nickel irruptive into its present shape, altered the shales within the basin to slates, and folded the overlying sediments. Then a regional fault system was developed to relieve the stresses. And after this: only the long slow process of erosion and, in modern times, glaciation. During the late stages of glaciation the basin was a glacial lake, which gave it the fertile soil cover that now makes the Sudbury basin good farmland.

It is a persuasive account. Yet scarcely a detail of it has gone unchallenged by the specialists. There are those who believe, for example, that the variegated components of the irruptive came from two separate chambers and were introduced at two separate times. There are also those who believe that the metal sulphides were present as another fraction of the reservoir, and were injected following the basaltic and granitic fractions.

And there is one whole group of geologists who have their own explanation for the original basin with its weakened circumference, which so localized and focussed the coming events. They say it was caused by a meteorite.

For evidence, they point to the shattered quartzite underlying everything else in the basin. They say it was shattered by impact. And then they point to the shatter-cones.

Shatter-cones are simply fractures in rock that outline the shape of a cone and are the result of shock. They have been discovered following nuclear tests in Nevada, where they form a concentric blast pattern with the points of the cones converging on the blast site, and the open ends facing outwards away from it. They have been found in the rocks surrounding the Sudbury basin for a distance of more than eight miles. Geologists who have studied them intimately say that if the formations in which they occur were to be unfolded and returned to their original attitudes, the shatter-cones would be found to radiate outward in a regular pattern, with their bases pointing back unerringly towards the Sudbury basin.

Their opponents say the shatter-cones could just as well have been produced by the explosive force of the ring of volcanoes. And they say, further, that if a meteor fell, it certainly picked itself a highly interesting spot – right there where so much was going to happen later. The point is that, though the rocks have been examined and mapped on the surface and underground in the mines; though volcanologists and geochemists and structural geologists and experts on mineral occurrences have all tried to sort the evidence; though this is one tiny area and though the study of it has gone on for nearly eighty years, no one yet has the whole answer.

It's the same everywhere on the Shield.

7 GRANITES AND GRANODIORITES

There's a familiar scene in the classic detective story: the sleuth has come to a dead end with the clues he has. So he sits down with a piece of paper (or a side-kick), sums up the evidence to date, casts about for anything he has overlooked – and comes up with an hypothesis that suggests a whole new line of attack.

Something similar happened in Shield geology between the two world wars. A thick dossier had been built up from the mappers' notes and the postage-stamp work in the mining areas, but the Shield's true nature seemed as mysterious as ever. In view of the Shield's scope, the clues were as scattered and incoherent as the greenstones and metasedimentary remnants themselves, scattered incoherently amid the wastes of granite and gneiss. How could they be correlated? What had been left out of account?

The answer was the granites and gneisses themselves. A fresh theoretical approach to the Shield was even now being supplied by two general discussions going on in geological circles. And one was a re-examination of the whole granite question.

Granite was supposed to be a very explicit kind of rock. It was supposed to consist of quartz, plus a feldspar containing either potash or soda, plus accessory minerals such as mica. And it was supposed to be an igneous intrusive. This required it to have welled upward into the country rock while still molten. Its characteristic coarse crystallinity was the badge of slow cooling while trapped short of the surface. And its clean sharp contacts with the country rock outlined the underground cooling-chamber. In the classroom, the definition was clear.

The trouble was that the definition failed to explain the special kinds of granitic material that occurred in Shield areas. There seemed to be, as a noted English geologist commented at a symposium in Ottawa, "granites and granites." In the Canadian Shield, for example, fully four-fifths of the rock was granitic either in composition or in texture.

It was true that many small bodies of textbook granite occurred in the Shield. The familiar domes that gave the Shield its "mammilated" look marked places where just such bodies of molten rock had welled upwards with enough force to warp the overhead rock. But these small stocks and plugs seemed to be associated with much larger bodies of igneous rock called batholiths. These were huge, often measuring miles in width and hundreds of miles in length. They were light-coloured and coarsely grained like the granite intrusives, but they were impure granodiorite rather than pure granite; the associated granites seemed almost like bubbles of lighter material that had risen from the general melt. Yet it was almost impossible to imagine the batholiths themselves as igneous intrusions. If they were, what had become of the rock mass previously there? Had the batholith pushed it all upwards and aside? The geologists in the field found no such evidence.

To add to the puzzle, the batholiths occurred like vast eddies in the midst of the familiar Shield gneisses and schists, and the contacts between the two were often very queer and suggestive. Sometimes the batholiths simply graded into gneiss. In other places it looked almost as though the batholith had eaten into the gneiss, choosing and digesting the necessary elements and rejecting the unwanted ones as wastes. Veinlets from the batholith reached out into the surrounding rock; bits of the border rock were included just inside the batholith; and the wastes could be detected in the form of a so-called basic front: an aureole of rejected basic elements concentrated in the country rock just ahead. And beyond, even at great distances from the batholith, the gneisses and schists often graded into what seemed to be granite, or else had granite sifted all through them.

After all the field notes had been compared and the theories discussed, a new notion had emerged: granitization. It was suggested that the Precambrian granites and granodiorites were not, in fact, virgin igneous rocks from the depths but instead had been reworked from older crustal material in some sort of giant melting-pot. Furthermore, the gneisses and schists had been in the same pot, though under rather less heat and pressure. But what, then, was the melting pot that could deform or completely granitize old crust on the Shield's vast regional scale? The answer lay in the other geological discussion that was going on at the same time: mountain-building.

New York geologists had been doing intensive work in the Appalachians. Other studies had been carried on in the Western Cordillera and in the European Alps. The mountain structures had been analysed both vertically and horizontally and now a tentative working model of regional mountain-building was being advanced to account for the observations.

The planetary processes at work remained unexplained, but the sequence of events seemed clear. In some unspecified way, the earth's crust downwarped into a trench or geosyncline all along a continental margin. On the seaward side, festoons of volcanic islands arose, and poured volcanics and lavas into the trench. On the landward side, great volumes of continental sediments were added to the filling. As the filling accumulated, the geosyncline prolapsed still deeper within the mantle, where it was subjected to great heat, and spasm after spasm of lateral pressure. Finally, though, the whole mass would shudder upwards, seeking equilibrium, and it would shoulder up adjoining blocks of continental crust into great peaks.

No one had ever seen into the keel of an active geosyncline; no one had ever penetrated the roots of an existing mountain range. But it was clear that here was a process equal to producing the streaky, congealed porridge of granitic and granodioritic material that was the very stuff of the Shield.

In 1913, a brilliant petrographer from the Survey named F. D. Adams had had a hunch. He was working in the band of glittering metasediments that began at the Sudbury basin and stretched from Georgian Bay eastward into Quebec. The metasediments were interfingered with altered volcanics. Surrounding them, mingling with them, was the familiar granodioritic Shield gneiss. Intruding them were small bodies of granite. He suggested that the whole great elongated system might be the exposed roots of an ancient mountain system.

But when the world-wide discussions on granites and mountain-building were over, it was clear that the whole Shield must somehow be made of mountain roots laid bare.

In fact James Gill of McGill University's Geology Department looked at the lifespan of a mountain system, the estimated length of Precambrian time and the extent of the Shield and estimated that, if one knew how to distinguish them, the Shield would prove to preserve the keels of between thirty and forty mountain systems. For the first time, two million square miles of granites and gneiss looked like making sense.

8 A STRUCTURAL COMPOSITE

The Geological Survey had been carrying out three grades of mapping in the Shield. One was the postage-stamp work: detailed mapping, fifteen hundred feet to the inch, of such locations of special interest as the Sudbury basin or Kirkland Lake.

The second grade of mapping was one mile to the inch. On this scale a field party could cover perhaps two hundred square miles. The third grade was reconnaissance mapping, four miles to the inch.

Then came the airplane. Even completion of the coarse-scale mapping could scarcely have produced more than a stilted and synthetic approximation of the view from a plane. Here were whole regions in relief; here was structural grain that could be traced for miles; here were formations with a sweep and continuity no one had imagined.

Already, correlating field data and their own hunches, a few geologists such as Professor James Gill of McGill University had been coming to the view that the Shield had structural subdivisions. An obvious example was the swathe of metasediments, including the marble, from Lake Huron through to Labrador.

But it was Tuzo Wilson, now Principal of Erindale College, University of Toronto, who came up with the most striking demonstration that the Shield was a structural composite. Wilson was a geophysicist. This was a new science that was seeking to determine the physical and mechanical principles at work on and in the earth, using such tools as mathematics, seismology, magnetics and the earth's gravity; geophysics focussed on the broad picture, the large scale, the synthesis of data. As early as 1930, when Wilson was a young assistant at the Geological Survey, he had seen the geological possibilities of the airplane, and he and his chief had even got the Air Force to give them some experimental flights. Now, at the end of World War II, he turned to the possibilities offered by aerial photographs. He set to work correlating aerial photographs of known areas with geological maps and notes of the same areas. The geological maps showed mainly the rock types encountered, plus known or suspected faults and folds. The notes gave additional details. In the photographs much was hidden by a mantle of forest of tundra, but certain features did show up clearly. These were the features with length called "linears" which were recognized by straight or gently curving valleys; ridges and escarpments; patterns of drainage. These linears could be correlated with the geological findings and could amplify them. For instance a fault had been encountered in field work and entered on the map: it could clearly be seen on the photograph, and what could also be seen was that it coincided with a valley that itself stretched straight and narrow beyond it. This suggested that the fault, too, might be extended, and a check in the field would prove this to be so. Or perhaps a single rock formation had been mapped as having been pinched into a long fold. The aerial photograph might show parallel rivers or chains of lakes in furrows alongside it, and other rivers or lakes, also parallel, at regular wave-lengths beyond. It could be confirmed in the field that all the rocks in the region had been thrown into regular parallel folds. In time Wilson was able to interpret the clues so accurately that he could even predict, from the photographs, what the geologists would find when they went into a new field. Small L-shaped lakes were the sign of characteristic blocky fracturing of underlying massive granite bodies. Where there was no overburden, patterns of concentric rings in the cover rock were the sign of domes where granite magma had punched up into them from below. A long narrow band of darker or lighter rock striping an outcrop was the sign of a tension crack through which molten rock had been able to intrude.

In forested country, the same formation sometimes showed up as a change in foliage, also visible from the air.

Where glaciers had advanced across the grain of the country they had acted to blur the pattern of the bedrock by filling in depressions with drift and rubble. Where they had followed the grain, they had deepened it by scouring action. The direction of the glacial advance was usually known; so its effects could be subtracted to leave the residual pattern of the bedrock.

This pattern could be interpreted with the aid of mechanic principles. For example, parallel regional folds were the result of pressure at right angles to the trend of the folds; the same pressure would also produce thrust faults.

Using a mosaic of photographs, Wilson put together an aerial montage of the Shield and translated this into a huge simplified map. On the map, using a child's coloured crayon, he began emphasizing all the major linears and interpreting them. When he had finished he had a structural subdivision of the Shield into five, and possibly six, areas each with its own structural grain. He called the areas sub-provinces, and gave each a name. And in each case Wilson suggested that major forces acting at right angles to the grain had been at work.

The southern centre of the Shield was named Superior sub-province. It was the vast familiar sweep of greenstones and gneisses and it turned out to stretch across northern Quebec, all of northern Ontario between Hudson Bay and Lakes Huron and Superior, and into Manitoba. The trend of the greenstone belts had been known to be east-west. So, it turned out, was the structural grain: the deforming pressures then had acted in a north-south direction.

To the west, the greenstone belts and the grain ceased abruptly in structural confusion at the Nelson River. Beyond, though the rocks of northern Saskatchewan and the District of Keewatin were relatively unknown, Wilson's map clearly showed a distinct northeast-southwest grain. Wilson called this Churchill sub-province. The opposing pressure must have come either from the southeast or northwest.

Beyond this again, among the Mackenzie Great Lakes was a complex and little-mapped area that might be one or possibly two sub-provinces. This area, which included Yellowknife, had belts of greenstones like those of Superior sub-province, though this time their trend was just to the east of due north.

On the other side of the Shield, in a broad arc following the Saint Lawrence Valley was the great glittering belt of metasediments and volcanics that cut off the trends of Superior sub-province as abruptly to the east, along the Grenville Front, as did the Nelson River to the west. This is the Grenville sub-province and, from its northeast trend, its northeast grain and its well-studied geology, it was determined that forces thrusting inward onto the Shield had caused the observed deformation.

In central Ungava forces also seemed to have thrust inwards and upwards onto the Shield. Wilson called this a sub-province too – Labrador – though the division was later refined.

Even this first tentative analysis of the Shield's overall structure was a major breakthrough. For the first time the unknown took on shape, could be seen to have an anatomy. There was an implication of evolution and sequence. There was a sense of epic: continental forces had been at work here. From such large effects the detectives might perhaps begin deducing some of the large causes that lay at the heart of the mystery.

Indeed, the impulse to begin speculating was almost irresistible. Wilson himself elaborated a proposition that might fit his observations. He accepted the view that the forces imposing the structural grain were great mountain-building forces. And from various sorts of evidence he concluded that Superior sub-province showed evidence of the earliest Precambrian mountain-building and that the other sub-provinces were younger. The conclusion he provisionally arrived at was that the area hidden by Hudson Bay was the original core of the continent. Onto the margins of this nucleus, he suggested, successive geosynclines had been welded: first Superior sub-province, and possibly the one in the far northwest; then Churchill sub-province and Grenville sub-province; then the one in Ungava. (In the high Arctic very little is even yet known of the relations of mountains bordering the Shield.) The idea was that the mountain-building forces always acted inward on the continental core. In Wilson's view at the time, as each geosyncline developed along the border of the nucleus, reared up into a mountain chain and was eroded back to the general level, it became part of a stable Shield.

And even after this, he suggested, the same stresses continued to operate: pressing inward on the Shield, raising its edges, depressing its centre in Hudson Bay. In Paleozoic times they had acted to thrust the great Appalachian geosyncline up onto the margins of the stable core. And most recently, the Western Cordillera had been welded on in the same way to the western margins of the continent. Thus North America had been built up by successive additions of mountain-welts to its borders.

The notion had one rather large implication: if this sequence were so, continents started small, with a nucleus, and grew by accretion. Therefore the supply of continental building material started small and was constantly being added to.

Newer findings in the Shield, and elsewhere, would shortly undermine this seductively neat and plausible account. The Shield has a habit of creating new puzzles out of apparent solutions. But the theory was a milestone nonetheless: it was the first attempt at a Shield storyline, the first attempt to find the working principle by which it had evolved.

As Wilson wrote at the time, "The air view gives one a grander view."

9 DATING THE OROGENIES

In deciding that Superior sub-province was the oldest, and that the others were successively younger, Tuzo Wilson had had the benefit of a handful of radiometric age-dates that had already been made on the Shield.

As early as the thirties a few age determinations had been made in the Shield using the decay-rate of uranium 238 to lead 206. Then, in 1948, the more reliable potassium-argon method was developed, and it began to look as though radiometric age-dates would be for Precambrian rocks what fossils were for more modern ones: a key to untangling and correlating widely separated formations. In 1960 the Geological Survey began a systematic programme of dating Shield rocks using this method on samples of mica from granitic rocks.

Some two thousand potassium-argon datings have been made, at a current rate of a couple of hundred a year. But even as early as 1961 it was evident that, far from distinguishing among the jumble of particular strata, the age-dates were continuing to lump them together. Indeed, prodigious sweeps of rock of many different kinds were in fact yielding approximately the same geologic dates.

Structural and other evidence made it clear that these were not the dates of the first cooling and emplacement of the rocks concerned. For example, the same date would be found in a granite pebble contained in a conglomerate and in the groundmass of the conglomerate itself. Yet the pebble must have weathered from a much older formation. Obviously what was being recorded by the radioactive clock was not rock birth but the date of some common crisis: some period when whole areas of different earlier histories had been heated to near the melting-point and then recrystallized. Virtually all the exposed rock in the Shield seemed to have undergone some such clock resetting crisis.

Furthermore, three singular clumpings of age-dates were turning up. One set of dates was clumped around 2.5 billion years ago. The second was clumped around 1.7 billion years ago. And the third was clumped just short of one billion years ago at 950 million years. The three peaks obviously represented

Glacial retreat

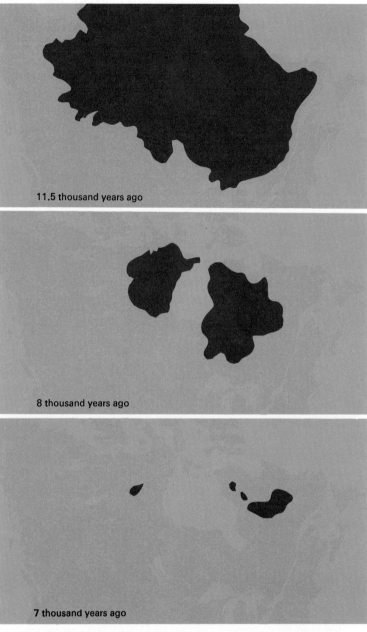

11.5 thousand years ago

8 thousand years ago

7 thousand years ago

Glaciation did not retreat northwards on the Canadian Shield at a uniform rate. The Great Lakes and the Arctic waters opened at about the same time, and two large inland centres, far from the moderating influence of water, were the last Shield areas to become free of the melting ice cover.

three crustal seizures – the long spasmodic convulsions of regional mountain-building that the geologists call "orogenies."

The geologists of the Survey christened the three orogenies revealed by the age-dates. The earliest one, the one that had peaked around 2.5 billion years ago, they called the Kenoran orogeny. The second, peaking at 1.7 billion years they called the Hudsonian orogeny. And the third, peaking just under a billion years ago, they called the Grenville orogeny – in honour of the sub-province along the north shore of the Saint Lawrence Valley whose rocks it had imprinted.

For indeed the age-dates were grouped not just in time but in space as well. Each had imprinted whole sectors of the Shield – and, strikingly, the sectors were much the same as those Tuzo Wilson had outlined on the structural evidence. The Shield was indeed subdivided. All the rocks from one of Wilson's suggested regions would show roughly the same dates. Then, sometimes across a boundary that was impressively sharp, all the rocks from an adjoining region would show a different date.

But even in the early stages of the dating programme one real peculiarity was showing up: the Shield subdivisions seemed to form a mosaic, rather than an orderly core-to-perimeter progression. In several cases the same age-dates seemed to have imprinted quite separate parts of the Shield.

It is only very recently, after a monumental labour of correlating dates with structure carried out by Dean C. H. Stockwell of the Survey, that this early impression has been confirmed and the whole pattern sorted out.

There are seven main divisions of the Shield. Because they are so distinct and so large they have now been upgraded to the status of geological provinces, with the whole Shield seen as a super-province. Two provinces were gripped by the earliest recorded orogeny, the Kenoran, with its date of 2.5 billion years. They are widely separated. One is Superior Province, which proves to stretch from the Nelson River on the west around Hudson Bay and up its east side almost as far as Cape Smith.

The second Kenoran-age province is called Slave Province and stretches northeast from Yellowknife to the mouth of the Coppermine River on the Arctic Ocean.

Yet a third area affected by the ancient Kenoran orogeny

has emerged: the very eastern edge of the Labrador Peninsula, fringing the North Atlantic, shows the same age-dates as Superior and Slave Provinces. But it has not been given the status of a province and has no name. Rocks just across Davis Strait in Greenland also show comparable dates.

The next great orogeny, the Hudsonian, has imprinted dates on no fewer than three provinces. The first is Churchill Province, and it proves to be of astonishing scope: it starts at the Nelson River, stretches north and east across the top of Hudson Bay to encompass most of the Boothia Peninsula and Somerset Island, all of Melville Peninsula and beyond, to the north, parts of Devon and Ellesmere Islands, before bending south and east again to take in almost all of Baffin Island, part of Southampton Island, the tip of Ungava, and a slice of Labrador. It is an incredible sweep of rock to have been deformed by the same episode. But there may be yet more; Churchill rock may underlie the sediments in the north half of Hudson Bay as well. And if this is true, then the sweep of Churchill Province is truly breathtaking.

The second province involved in the Hudsonian orogeny is Bear Province, the northwest tip of the Shield isolated from the rest by the older Slave Province. It, too, has outliers in the Arctic: along the continental coast near Darnley Bay, and up in Victoria Island.

The third province affected by the Hudsonian orogeny is called Southern Province. Only a bit of it lies in Canada: a wedge of rock from Lake Huron's North Channel pointing up to Sudbury; and some shreds and patches along the north shore of Lake Superior.

The third great orogeny on the Shield, and the most recent from the geological point of view, is recorded only in the province that bears its name, the Grenville. The geological province includes the Adirondack region, a ten thousand square mile area of New York State, which is joined to it across the Saint Lawrence by a neck of rock, called the Frontenac Axis, that surfaces in the river as the Thousand Islands. Otherwise, Grenville Province stretches in a long clean belt, more than a thousand miles long and as much as two hundred miles wide, that parallels the Saint Lawrence clear to the Labrador coast.

Three orogenies and six provinces. But in Stockwell's work

of correlation a seventh province has unexpectedly shown up. Its rocks show ages that cluster around 1,370 billion years, which means that they were recrystallized before the Grenville rocks (at .95 billion years) but after either Churchill rocks (at 1.7 billion years) or Superior rocks (at 2.5 billion years). Yet it is a triangular island of rock bounded by the rocks of all three. It is called Nain Province, and it is in eastern Labrador.

The only possible conclusion is that Nain, too, was involved in an orogeny, but one that was reflected nowhere on the Shield save in this small, isolated oddly-shaped area. It has been called the Elsonian orogeny and is placed between the earlier Hudsonian and later Grenville orogenies.

That is the age-date picture of the Shield – and it could scarcely be more maddening or ambiguous. So far as is known, the only way you can get the interfingered volcanics and sediments, the grades of metamorphosis, the intricacies of folding, the crystalline wastes of gneiss, the granodiorite batholiths and the domes of upwelling granite that are the very stuff of the Shield is by mountain-building. Only mountain-building, it seems, could subject rocks to the heat and pressure that could recrystallize them completely and, recrystallizing them, reset the radio-active clocks to record the event.

Yet the provinces suggest mountain-building events unlike any that have been visualized. Look at Superior Province, marked by the Kenoran orogeny. Certainly *something* happened to give all its structures their prevailing east-west trends and to freeze its rocks at one telltale date. Yet this is an area far greater than any mountain belt of modern times – and an area that is the wrong shape, to boot. Superior Province is no long, narrow geosyncline. And what is its relationship to those far-off, fringing rocks on the Labrador coast, with their echoing imprint? Why does Slave Province, in the far northwest, yield the same age-dates, though its rocks give evidence of pressure from another direction? What kind of mountain-building was this?

Or look at the extraordinary hemispherical sweep of Churchill Province – and at Bear and Southern Provinces, contemporary to Churchill but quite unrelated to it in space. Look at the anomalous hemmed-in triangle of Nain Province.

They are, these earlier provinces, like stray jigsaw pieces arbitrarily jammed together without much regard for puzzle subject. Only Grenville Province, a sort of late-Precambrian postscript, has the length and continuity and correct fringing position of a textbook geosyncline. The age-dates may have confirmed the structural subdivision of the Shield, but they scarcely support any pleasant theory of early continental growth by the orderly accretion of mountain-belts around a core.

Indeed the dates are now suggesting something very like the reverse. It has been known for a long time that Precambrian rock dips beyond the Shield margins to form a basement layer for other, later, deposits of rock; for example, it is exposed at the bottom of the rock succession in the Grand Canyon. The fact was acknowledged without particularly being pursued. But new work in the Western Cordillera has revealed granite intrusions with dates of 675-970 million years, and, at the great lead-zinc mine at Kimberley, British Columbia, leads with dates of 1.25 billion years. And now, it seems, there are rocks caught up among the roots of the Cordillera that are even older than these. Somehow they have escaped the recrystallization that, over in the Shield, has obliterated everything before the Kenoran orogeny – and they yield dates of 3.2 billion years.

The earth scientists have arrived at a tentative date for the earth's beginning. Working from uranium-lead calculations, from theory about the solar system, and from age-dates of meteorites that were probably by-products of the solar system's birth, they have decided that the planet came into being no more than six billion years ago, and probably closer to 4.5 billion. Allow some time – say a billion years – for the beginnings of a crust to form, wherein a record could be left. And so: put the beginning of geological time at 3.5 billion years ago.

These rocks among the roots of the Cordillera, then, come from very near the start of things. As Robert Folinsbee of the University of Alberta commented dryly, in the *Canadian Upper Mantle Report*, 1967, "This observation rules out the possibility that all of the Canadian Cordillera accreted to the continent of North America in post Precambrian time, and suggests that the general outline of the continent has not changed much in the course of geologic time."

A widespread Precambrian crust, and an apparent record of piecemeal mountain-building: because of the age-date evidence, any theories about the nature and development of the Shield – and of continents – must somehow account for these.

10 THE GREENSTONE WHORLS

The wholesale recrystallization of Shield rock in a succession of orogenies might seem to have brought the investigators face to face with a blank wall. How could anyone probe past such clue-obliterating events?

Yet it is being done. In a recent and elegant display of geological detection, for example, Dr. Hugh Wynne-Edwards of Queen's University examined a cross-section of the mountain roots exposed in Grenville Province and recognized most of the rocks as having been in place long before the Grenville orogeny. In fact, once the disguising imprint of the Grenville convulsion had been subtracted, great stretches of gneiss could clearly be identified as extensions of Superior Province, next door. Wynne-Edwards had penetrated the disguise by using "feel" and the findings of chemistry. For space-age chemistry can deduce what rock elements went into a crucible and, in many cases, in what order. It can tell a good deal about how high the heat was, and how great the pressure, and how slow or fast the cooling. And a companion to chemistry in pushing past the age-date barrier is the common sense about rocks and their habits and textures and histories that only long experience in the field can give. Indeed the dual method has been used to push back, even past the Kenoran orogeny, to the remote Archaean events of the Shield's earliest youth.

Dr. Alan Goodwin, of the University of Toronto, is a specialist in the old volcanic remnants of the Shield. In at least four places in the Shield, the old greenstone pods and remnants seem to form a crude pattern of whorls surrounding a nucleus of gneisses. In Slave Province, on the northwest corner of Hudson Bay, and in western Ungava, the pattern is deformed and cramped. But it can be chemically proved that the Superior greenstones overlap into Churchill Province and, once this link is made, the greenstone pattern in Superior Province is surprisingly spacious and clear. Six east-west belts, three to the north and three to the south, bracket an apparent nucleus on the Ontario-Manitoba border.

Early in his career Goodwin was engaged in mining exploration. Since most of the noble-metal occurrences are associated with the greenstone belts of the Archaean provinces, he got to know them well and it was perhaps natural that his later choice of research should be their systematic study and analysis.

He came to a major and most unexpected conclusion: the Superior greenstones had almost the appearance of fresh volcanics such as those of Hawaii.

Given the nature of the home terrain, Canadian geologists hadn't hitherto been especially knowledgeable about volcanics. In the general setting of the Shield and the particular setting of the Archaean provinces, it had generally been assumed that the greenstones, like the general gneisses and schists, had been deeply buried, profoundly metamorphosed, rendered plastic, tied in knots and otherwise altered out of recognition and diagnosis.

Instead, Goodwin recognized textures and structures very like those of lava that had just poured into the sea. There were, for example, intact pillow lavas, the sign of underwater deposition. And chemistry made it clear that the green tinge which supplied their name was the sign of only very mild metamorphosis. These greenstones could scarcely have been downwarped into the keel of a geosyncline. Instead, it was almost as though they had ridden high and unscathed all through Shield history. The idea was startling, and it had a great many implications. Among them was the probability that they still reflected their original location and distribution.

After studying the greenstones of the Shield, Goodwin now thinks the primary stage of crustal formation was the surfacing of a widespread scum of light granitic material over the surface of the earth. This would have worked upwards by gravity differentiation from the mantle, and it would be thin and easily ruptured. Over this scum a shallow continuous sea would already have formed.

Then, for some reason, pairs of island-arc formations began to fracture the granitic film. Volcanoes are really just thermal centres: perhaps they began to occur wherever there were localized hot spots in the mantle. First there would be a widespread underwater oozing of dark basic lava to form a platform perhaps two to three miles thick, complete with pillow structures. Then, through vents in the platform, cones would start to build. These would push up in pulses of activity until finally they pushed above sea level and exploded with lava, ash and

LIFE IN THE BUSH

Life for mammals on the Shield can be described as survival of the fittest. In addition to coping with the severity of the sub-arctic winter, many small and medium-sized animals have to face such predators as the timber wolf which itself is in danger of extinction.

Shield inhabitants

The main species of animal life in the Shield can be found near the southern edges, in the forested areas where life is easier and food more readily available. The largest single group is made up of the rodents — various mice, voles, lemmings as well as beavers, muskrats and porcupines. The carnivores — marten, wolves, black bears and lynx — constitute the second largest group, followed by the ruminants — moose, deer and caribou. Several kinds of shrews and moles also scurry about. An eastern chipmunk (1) is shown busily looking for food to add to his stock, which he will waken from time to time to eat during winter hibernation. Moose (2) prefer to stay near shallow lakes and swamps where they can duck for lily-shoots in summer. The antlers are shed in the winter, but grow quickly all summer so that by rutting season in fall the bull moose is well equipped to do battle over a mate. A bullfrog (3) squats near the shoreline of a pond ready to devour an unsuspecting insect, bird or smaller frog. The white-tailed deer (4) is well-known in southern areas across the Shield, but now seems to be extending its range farther north. Black bear twins (5) occur quite frequently, and these fuzzy cubs will reach maximum size at about six years of age. Adaptations to help cope with great extremes of temperature, and with the winter shortage of food, have had to be made by most Shield animals. Some, the true hibernators, spend the bleakest months in a death-like sleep, while others wake occasionally to eat. A thick layer of fat is often developed just under the skin as further protection against the cold.

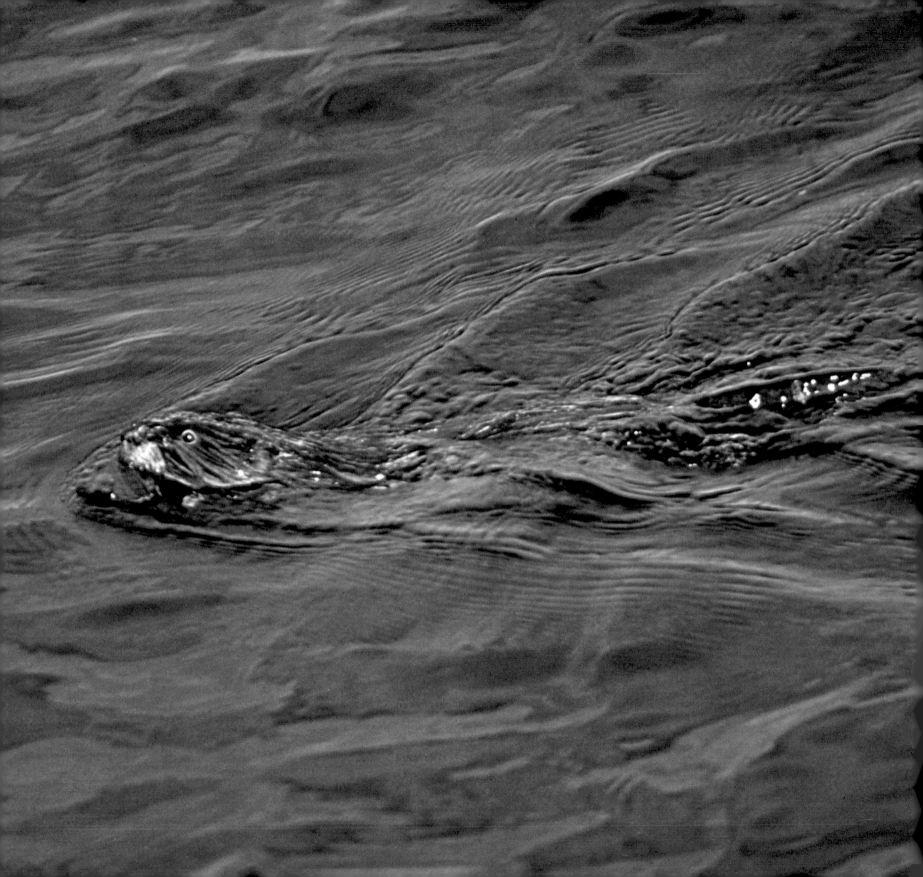

broken fragments of rock. Just such explosive volcanic debris has been traced among the greenstones. Each pair of island-arcs would bracket and isolate a node of the original granitic film, and along their outer edges basins of deposition would deepen to receive the lavas, the volcanic fragmentals and, finally, sediments from the eroding cones.

Then, perhaps because the growing loads in these marginal dumps were too much for the granitic scum to bear, the crust would fracture again, and outer pairs of island-arcs would break through, and so on. Each granitic nucleus together with its surrounding volcanic belts and trenches would be a crustal node, a centre of crustal thickening, a protocontinent. It would be possible for two nearby protocontinents to interfere with each other, and Goodwin speculates that this is the explanation of the cramped and ill-developed appearance of the Slave, Hudson Bay and Ungava remnants. Volcanic activity would weld them together before the pattern was very far advanced. But with room to grow, the crustal nodes could develop sequentially until broad, stable platforms had been achieved. The greenstones of Superior Province look to Goodwin like the embedded growth-rings of such a platform.

And then what? At this point Goodwin invokes a process that one or two other geologists have also come to consider possible: crustal underplating. In the same way that the first granitic scum formed, further differentiates from the mantle kept being added to the underside of the protocontinents. If one such protocontinent wasn't anchored or welded to other protocontinents and could attain freeboard, it might simply rise as the crust thickened from below, bearing passively aloft the formations at its surface in a condition as fresh as the Superior greenstones. It is perhaps worth noting that there are almost identical fresh greenstone complexes in the Archaean of Australia.

If Goodwin is right, then something very close to the original crust of the earth has at last been recognized in the Shield.

Muskrats, although they are quite awkward when moving about on land, are expert swimmers, and use their vertically flattened tails as rudders to guide them through the water. Although they feed mainly on plant material, muskrats also eat flesh and use their forefeet to pry open clam shells to get at the tasty meal inside.

11 CONTINENTAL DRIFT

At Expo 67 in Montreal, one May night, Professor Tuzo Wilson gave a lecture to a small private audience of science writers and dignitaries. During his lecture he kept on the stage with him a boiling pot of tomato soup. Like any other pot of boiling soup, this one floated on its surface a froth that had risen from below, grown with time, and piled upon itself as its water content evaporated. Wilson was using it to dramatize a revolutionary new concept of the earth and its behaviour.

The froth on the tomato soup, Dr. Wilson explained, would someday soon be recognized as analogous to the continents of the earth: islands of atypical, differentiated, granitic scum at the mercy of the currents in the pot. The clear, churning broth itself was behaving as the earth's interior is now believed to do, in a viscous layer beginning perhaps thirty-seven miles beneath the crust and reaching to depths of 155 miles or so. The evidence that there are convection currents in the mantle is, as Dr. Wilson and a great many other earth scientists believe, becoming more convincing every day. So, too, is the evidence that the continents have moved about in response to the currents.

It was soon after the discovery of America that men noticed how neat a jigsaw-fit the opposite coasts of the Atlantic would give if they were brought together. Then, sixty years ago, a German meteorologist named Alfred Wegener began to give this apparent romancing serious consideration. Wegener pointed out three reasons for believing that parts of the earth's crust might be moving around. The first reason was, precisely, the excellent fit of some pairs of opposite coasts – notably those of the Atlantic Ocean and those of the Red Sea.

The second reason was the well-known but baffling evidence that climatic zones of the past had been displaced. There were unmistakable signs of glaciation in the tropics, and of coral reefs, rich coal deposits and oil wells as far north as Spitsbergen, Greenland and Alaska. It was in many ways simpler and more elegant to imagine that the continents had moved around than that ice had once covered the equator while tropical seas covered the pole.

Wegener's third reason had to do with glaciation and glacial rebound. If the rigid crust could sink under a load of ice, and spring back when the load was removed – as stranded beaches and other evidence strongly suggested – then it was behaving like something that floats.

But the recent exploration and magnetic mapping of the ocean floors has made convection – or at least some sort of sub-crustal flow – not just a possibility but a logical necessity. For the ocean floors have been discovered to unroll outwards, like twin conveyor belts, from the mid-ocean ridge systems. The rate and direction of flow has been measured in most of the oceans, and a tentative global model of present ocean floor spreading or closing, and of accompanying continental migrations, has been established.

In this model, currents in the mantle well up along the mid-ocean ridges; they subside at the mobile zones that border continents and oceans, carrying down with them plates of oceanic crust to be re-cycled. Thus the ocean floors have been renewed through time. But continents are too light and rigid to be sucked under, so they are simply rafted around at the mercy of the currents. Mountain ranges are the bow waves that are thrust up along their leading edges as they are borne along.

If new currents start up, ridges open in new places, and the ocean floors begin spreading from them. Such a ridge, perhaps only ten million years old, has just broken through in the southern Pacific. It roughly parallels the coast of South America, meets North America at lower California, and may be about to split Baja California away along the Gulf of California. If the currents start up under a land mass rather than under an ocean, they may tear it apart, creating a new ocean basin: Africa is starting to break up along the Red Sea and rift valleys.

Just as the mid-ocean ridges are the crustal expression of the upwelling currents, so the mobile zones are the crustal expression of the downturn. They are zones of mixing, weakness and regeneration, marked by ocean trenches such as the Mindanao Deep or the Tuscarora Deep or the Puerto Rico Deep; the trenches are bordered to landward by volcano chains and island-arcs, and are the site of deep-seated earthquakes. And any continent caught on the surface of a convecting cell is inexorably carried towards them to hang, in a position of poise, right over the line of sink. But as it arrives at the volcanoes and island-arcs above the trench it overrides them and incorporates them in its bow-wave of mountains. And so there is a global pattern of unrest, which begins with expansion at ocean ridges, where new oceanic crust is created, and ends with retraction and downturning at the continental margins, where old continental crust is mixed with fresh volcanics and thus regenerated. And so the continents persist – even while they are shouldered and battered through the eons into ever-changing shapes and new configurations. Asia has just joined Europe, and India has piled into it from the south, thrusting up the Himalayas. The Atlantic Ocean, which once was closed, is opening now. North America has just overridden part of the East Pacific Rise and is drifting northwest at a measured rate of twenty feet per hundred years.

It is all too new, really, for the whole model to be more than speculative. There are lifetimes of data and measurement to be collected, designs to be worked out, patterns of movement to be established – not just for the present but back through time. And then all geology will have to be rewritten. For in the meantime, as Tuzo Wilson himself wrote recently, "It will be very unwise to write . . . any accounts of large regions in shields or mountains without realizing that rocks now contiguous may bear no relation to one another, that the off-shore sources of old sediments may have been carried far away and that the sources of igneous rocks need not have remained beneath them."

And when the task is done, what will have been learned about the Shield? Well, perhaps, why there is a Hudson Bay, and why Greenland seems to have broken off from Labrador. Why there are stretch marks all over the Shield, and one place where it seems nearly to have been pulled asunder, or else squeezed in a vice. How such a mosaic of provinces came to be together, and whether they were once separate, and if so, what process cemented them together. Why Nain Province seems so alien and hemmed-in. And why the great seizures of orogeny occurred, and where the Shield was heading at the time and what, perhaps, it bumped into. And before that, whether Goodwin's protocontinents, too, were rafted around like bits of scum to come haphazardly together at last. And many other answers to questions not yet dreamed of.

And that will be Part Two of the detective story.

LAND OF LAKES AND FORESTS

The water trap

Bogs are a common feature of the hard granite rock areas of the Shield where the land has been stripped bare of its soil and left scoured and ill-drained from the great glacial advances and retreats. All bogs are accumulations of peat with slow water circulation: the surface water is from rain, which is poor in salts, and the peat absorbs all dissolved material; moreover, the granitic bedrock provides almost no minerals to the groundwater flowing through it. The raised bog (upper) is formed from the accumulation of dead sphagnum creating a layer of peat; the unique water-absorbent qualities of the sphagnum draw the ground-water upward

CROSS-SECTION OF A RAISED BOG

and, in cases where the moss is abundant, actually raise the water-table. Once the peat has absorbed sufficient water, surplus rainfall gathers around the edges of the dome-shaped bog which, thus watered, grows upward and outward. Growth on the bog stops when evaporation from the surface balances the rainfall and upward flow of groundwater. The low, ordinary, quaking bogs (lower) form in shallow, clearwater lakes and barren hollows and occur through the gradual deposition of various organic materials. Frequently, streams dump silt into the lakes, and plants along the water's edge add their own debris. Further materials such as run-off from the land above the lake help eventually to obliterate the lake, and finally the mud on the bottom becomes firm enough to support shrubs and, then, trees. Pools left in the middle of the lake may be bridged by plants like sedge. Ultimately, stands of black spruce on the edge of the lake creep out from the shore and shade the bog until the lake is converted into woodland.

Organic deposits

Peat accumulation

Granitic bedrock

Peat accumulation

Granitic bedrock

RAISED BOG

Plants other than sphagnum grow on the surface of the oxygen-poor raised bog, and endure long after bog growth has been stunted. Heather or other related shrubs may grow on the stabilized surface, but few trees are to be seen. Forest growth on or around a raised bog indicates a recent change towards a much drier climate.

QUAKING BOG

The conversion of a lake to a bog is marked by certain ecological zones where plants suggest both the time and extent of bog growth. Pondweed (a) grows in deeper water, pondweed with floating leaves (b) in shallows. Loose-strife (c) forms a floating mat which allows the spread of bog rosemary (d), sphagnum (e) and leatherleaf (f). Where the ground is drier, black spruce (g), cotton-grass (h) and sedge (i) prosper, followed by shining willow (j) and smooth alder (k). At the edge of the bog is a forest of larch (l) and red spruce (m). A shallow ditch of water marks the original shoreline beyond which grow dry-land trees such as white birch (n).

The beaver lodge is a masterpiece of construction, complete with underwater exit tunnel, air hole, and sleeping shelves.

The dam builders

Industrious, sociable animals, beavers live in close, co-operative units. From midsummer until almost winter, the family presents a scene of diligent activity, working towards a single end – to provide food and shelter against the winter cold. A dam is built to raise the water level and bring more food and building material within floating distance. When a lodge made of branches and saplings has been raised, the entire dome is plastered with mud, except for an air hole left at the top. Plenty of food for the winter is stored underwater near the exit tunnel. Canada's largest rodent has many adaptations for aquatic life: (1) folds of skin around the mouth keep water out; (2) under water, valves seal ears and nostrils automatically, transparent eyelids provide excellent vision; (3) a split toe-nail on each hind foot helps groom the fur and retain streamlining; (4) the long, flat, scaly tail acts as a rudder; the webbed hind feet provide propulsion; (5) the three-inch long gnawing teeth are worn down with use, but never stop growing.

70

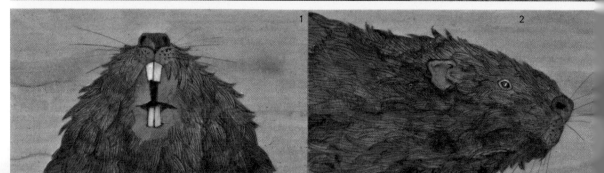

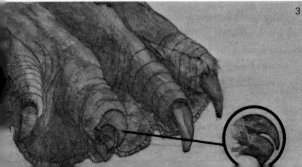

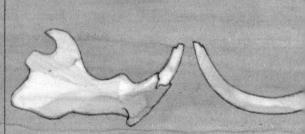

3

4

Death in the shallows

Throughout the Shield region in summertime, the northern pike's favourite haunt is amongst the weedy shallows of lakes, where it often hangs absolutely still just below the surface, awaiting its prey. The pike is not too fussy about what it eats, and with a large mouth full of long, sharp teeth, will devour fish of all kinds, insects, even small muskrats and small ducks. There is a common belief that the pike, one of our most popular game fish, sheds its teeth in summer and grows a new set. However, studies show that broken teeth are individually replaced, and this replacement process assures the pike an efficient set of canines at all seasons of the year. Cross-sections at right (1, 2) illustrate a replacement tooth developing in a pike's lower jaw. After a tooth has been broken off, its bony base is resorbed, leaving a square gap. A new base is formed of soft tissue, which later hardens and becomes firmly attached to the flat surface of the jaw. As it enlarges, the base also unites with the inner edge of the jaw, and, filling the entire tooth-supporting section of its space, the base becomes square. Simultaneously, the needle-like tip moves outward, slanting slightly backwards, and becomes exposed above the gum, its edges razor-sharp. The pike's sensory pores, used in much the same way as the human sense of smell, are located on each side of the lower jaw (3). The northern pike (4, top) and the muskellunge (4, bottom), another member of the pike family, are often mistaken for each other, but they can be distinguished by the differences in scaling of the cheeks and opercles. Newly born pike fry remain in shallow water for several weeks, eating tiny water fleas. However, the fry are cannibalistic (5) and soon begin to set upon other fry born in the area that are almost equal in size.

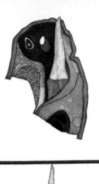

1

2

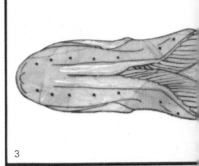

3

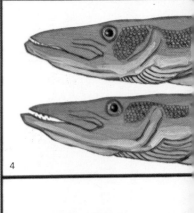

4

5

A place for everything

The boreal forest is a fascinatingly complex, constantly changing community of trees and animals. Various types of forest growth occur, each in its own way moving toward a climax forest, and each individually associated with certain species of birds and other animals. Climax forests, which are becoming increasingly rare under the pressure of civilization, contain their own special community of life. Burnt over and cut over areas are much more common as are the species that inhabit them.

Moose

Beaver

Canada Lynx

Nashville Warbler

Lincoln's Sparrow

Porcupine

Red-eyed Vireo

Timber Wolf

Open Pond

Black Bear

Otter

Timber Wolf

Black Bear

Cutting Clearing

Yellowthroat

White-tailed Deer

Striped Skunk

Semi-open forest environment, caused by logging, is a common forest habitat and is inviting to many species. This setting, because of the penetration of the sun's rays, contains much plant growth.

Open ponds and swampy clearings in the forest provide an excellent habitat for amphibious creatures such as the beaver and the otter, as well as the huge moose. The Canada lynx and timber wolf prey upon the moose.

Timber Wolf

Black-backed
Three-toed
Woodpecker

Black Bear

Climax
Forest

Blackburnian

White-tailed Deer

American Redstart

Tennessee Warbler

After a Fire

Striped Skunk

Yellow Warbler

Marten

Woodland Caribou

Areas recovering from fire contain the black bear, the white-tailed deer, and many other animals. Although the intense heat of a major forest fire usually kills all but the largest trees, plants and animals are soon re-established.

A climax forest attracts the woodland caribou, because in this environment the caribou finds abundant growth of his favourite food, lichens. Warblers such as the Tennessee and black-burnian sing from treetops in a mature forest.

Family life

The distinctive, throaty howl of timber wolves is often heard in Canada's Algonquin Park, which has perhaps one of the world's largest wolf populations. Despite the fearsome tales long associated with wolves, causing them to be hunted ceaselessly, there is no substantiated record of any Park camper ever being attacked by these animals which in fact possess many of the habits of the domestic dog. Living, travelling and hunting in packs, wolves are gregarious and affectionate amongst themselves, and, when the pups are born in early summer, the whole pack helps to care for them, first swallowing food and regurgitating it later to feed the pups. Wolves are creatures of the open forest spaces and the den, a cave or an abandoned beaver lodge, is mostly used for rearing the pups. Each pack has its own territory, and each wolf has a social standing within the pack - a member indicates his dominance by holding his head and tail high when approaching another. Wolves depend mainly on large mammals for food but by usually hunting sick or weak animals and seldom killing more than they need, wolves make a vital contribution to the balance of nature.

Dominant wolf

Wolf regurgitating
to feed pups

PART THREE / **PLANT LIFE**

12 THE PIONEERING LICHENS

The first plants to come back to the naked Shield after the glaciers melted must have been the lichens, for the lichens specialize in living where nothing else can. They are the pioneers. And in many places they are still in possession of the land.

There is a field of loose shingle near the Montreal River that was once the beach of a glacial lake. It is so porous that rain simply disappears into it. Yet scarcely a square inch of the field is bare of lichen mats, some of them as much as a foot thick. They must have been growing there almost since the ice disappeared, and still no other plant life has come to dispossess them. In the same way lichens carpet the taiga – that bitter savannah of scattered, stunted spruce clumps that marks the transition from boreal forest to tundra. And lichens alone make up the ground cover over most of the tundra itself. Wherever the living is hard some species of lichen has domain. And so, from south to north the lichens map all the rawest or harshest or most hostile environments of the Shield.

Lichens (pronounced "likens") can stand tropical heat, and they can also withstand cold that would kill any other form of vegetation. Lichens have been exposed for hours in the laboratory to temperatures approaching -459.69°F, which is absolute zero, and have afterwards been revived to resume normal life. In fact some species flourish best below the freezing point. Lichens can also outwit drought, for they simply wait until it ends. Only absolute aridity kills them: no lichens grow in the centre of the Egyptian desert. But nearer the borders of Israel a bit of dew forms each day at dawn and sunset and there the lichens are. Lichens are the first colonists on lava beds. They go higher in the Himalayas than all other plants. They can be found on outcrops not far from the north pole, and they are almost the only plant life in all Antarctica. Because they have emancipated themselves from the need for soil, they can grow on frozen ground, or under the snow, or on burning sand, or on bare rock. They need very little to live on, light, moisture, and a place to anchor.

The lichens' secret is that they are symbionts: plant partnerships entered into by two unrelated organisms each of which has something the other needs.

To some people, the idea of symbiosis is a science-fiction horror. To others, symbiosis is a perfect symbol for the whole concept of ecology, of the intimate and crucial interdependence of every part of life. In either case it is an extraordinary evolutionary development – and it was brought off somewhere along the line by representatives from two of the most primitive plant forms still in existence: the alga and the fungus.

The algae in the lichen relationship are either blue-green or green algae – little scraps of a protoplasm from exactly the same aquatic family that first acquired chlorophyll and invented photosynthesis back in the Precambrian era. Most algae still live perfectly successfully by themselves in nature. Indeed everywhere there is moisture and a bit of sunlight, the algae are using solar energy plus water plus carbon dioxide to make starch plus oxygen. Blue-green ones, for example, can be found on the north side of trees in a wet wood. And it seems almost certain that the particular algae in the lichen partnership, mostly a race called *Trebouxia*, can also live free in nature, though they are not common. But, like all algae, they must have water. They can't live where it's dry, or where the sunlight is too fierce.

The other partner comes from the strange group of plants that can go only where other life is already established, for that is what they feed on: dead or living organisms. They are the fungi, a sort of plant underworld of parasites and scavengers. This is the family of the moulds and mushrooms, of penicillin and the puffball and yeast and ergot and the truffle. They do not have green colouring because they have no chlorophyll. They cannot make their own food; so they live on whatever can. They secrete a whole range of digestive enzymes and with these they dissolve and absorb the food-substances with which they come in contact. The relationship is hostile, and often fatal for the host, for the fungus, any fungus, lives at the expense of something else. Except, that is, for the lichenized fungus.

The particular kinds of fungus that have entered into the lichen partnership don't seem to occur alone in nature. And various attempts in the laboratory to make the fungus component grow by itself have scarcely been successes. The spores have sprouted, and have kept growing as long as they had food, but it was a moron growth: a pallid mass of tangled filaments, without purpose or structure. Far from being hostile, the lichenized fungus is aimless and ineffective without its alga partner.

But in combination, these fungi and these algae have achieved a new life-form. It is the nearest thing to a closed system, a self-contained and self-sustaining unit, that the vegetable kingdom has produced. The fungus component catches and stores the water vital to the algae. The photosynthesizing algae, in return, feed the fungus. And the plant they have turned themselves into, in order to do this, looks like neither component but instead has its own appearance – and its own rules of behaviour. It even has its own method of reproduction, unlike that of either original partner. True, some lichens produce fungus-like fruiting bodies and spores. But the habit is thought to be no more than a vestigial reflex, for the spores, like the ones in the laboratory, cannot produce a new lichen. Instead, the lichen's true method of reproduction is not sexual but vegetative: any windborne fragment of the plant body, called the thallus, can start a new lichen colony. Indeed if the habitat is favourable they can spread very quickly. A dark film of lichens formed over sand dunes in Alberta in only a few seasons. But they have also mastered the trick of biding their time. When conditions are bad they stay inactive, creeping ahead only when there is enough light and food and moisture to do so. Members of a recent expedition to Antarctica found lichens on one face of a cairn exactly as described by an expedition thirty years earlier; in that time they had not even spread to the other faces of the cairn. Lichens normally spread along what might be called a leading-edge, or growth front, leaving their degenerative parts behind or below as a tangle of dead threads. Because of this, and because of their capacity for slow growth, they are in theory immortal. Certainly some of the ones on the Shield are thousands of years old.

No one knows exactly how this strange symbiotic partnership first got started. But there have been attempts to synthesize lichens in the laboratory from the separate alga and fungus components, and these have shown one fascinating thing. As long as there is enough light and moisture, the algae develop and reproduce normally. And as long as food is present in the culture medium, the fungus spores, too, germinate and grow in their peculiar mindless fashion. And they pay no attention to the algae. But if they are starved, if they have to live for a few weeks on nothing but air and sterile water, parts of the growth become bloated, and other parts straggle weakly. They grow visibly sickly with malnutrition. And at this point they put out short side branches that grapple the algae. After a month, the algae are woven right into the dense tangle of fungal filaments: and far from being killed or weakened, they continue to flourish. What is more, the formless growth has begun to show a structure. The fungal filaments have begun to organize themselves into something closer to the texture of lichen tissue. Parts have become thickened and dense in a way that suggests the rind or cortex of some true lichens. And the algal cells show signs of being localized into the food-producing layer that is characteristic.

That is as far as the lichen synthesizers have been able to go, but it is far enough to suggest what one researcher has called "the tremendous accident." Perhaps at some early evolutionary stage, a few races of algae such as *Trebouxia*, and some primitive species of fungus, were being crowded out by more aggressive algae and fungi. In the face of starvation and extinction, perhaps they came together by accident, to victimize each other – the alga seeking moisture, and shelter from the parching sunlight; the fungus seeking food – and found they could live together in truce. And perhaps, what is more, they found the partnership had unique strengths, a special mobility, a self-sufficiency that allowed survival where no other plant form could live. And so the pioneering lichens came to be.

The relationship is still delicate. Algae have certainly been overwhelmed by a fungus partner grown suddenly all-consuming in the presence of abundant food. And in the presence of surplus moisture over a long period the algae may revert to their free-living aquatic form, outstripping the fungus. Even in poise, behaving as a single organism, the lichen is sensitive to certain kinds of changes. One species, specific to the bases of trees, was experimentally transplanted five feet upwards to the centre of the trunk. Without exception, every transplanted lichen died. Each species, it seems, is highly specific to its chosen conditions, and is extremely vulnerable to changes in micro-climate. And this is the one weakness: they yield to competition without much fight.

There are countless species of lichens but they take three main forms, each more sophisticated than the last. The most primitive and the most prevalent is the crustose form. In its more inconspicuous versions it would be easy to miss its presence, for it can appear to be no more than a greyish-green bloom on the trunk of a tree, or the discolouring of age on a rock face. Such lichens have been called "time stains." They are mere films

Plant succession on the Shield

Lichens exist on bare rock surfaces where no other plants can grow. Composed of two plants — a fungus and an alga — which co-exist (symbiosis), these pioneers reproduce vegetatively: some produce dustlike particles (soredia) in which a few algal cells are surrounded by a web of fungal hyphae (a) which are borne by the wind and may develop into new lichens. Lichens also reproduce when small pieces break off (b) or when the top layer fragments (c) and individual pieces blow away. Gradually, the lichens wear away the rock until it is useable soil, thus preparing the way for moss growth.

Fungus
Fungal hyphae
Alga
Rock
Cross-section of lichen thallus

Fungus
Alga
(a) soredia forced outward
(b) small particles fragment
(c) outer layer breaks up

Mosses, like the twisted moss, grow on decomposed rocks, worn down by the lichens. Capsules (a) produce moss spores (b) that escape and, if they land on sufficiently moist ground, will swell while a thin green thread (protonema) (c) emerges. Gametophytes (d) develop on the protonema, independent plants of both sexes (e, f). Sperm from the male organ (antheridium) (g) swims to the egg of the female organ (archegonium) (h) to form a zygote which divides many times to form the embryo sporophyte (i), usually a long stalk (j) with a capsule at its top (k).

Twisted Moss

Tamarack, a member of the larch family of trees, grows on moist, boggy soils, prepared for fertility by the lichens and mosses; thus the tamarack carries the cycle of plant succession on exposed rock surfaces one step further. The tree, found in the cooler parts of the northern hemisphere, can grow to eighty feet, though its usual height is between 40 and 50 feet. The wood of these tall, straight trees is important for lumber and in construction. The tamarack bears small ovoid cones, and, unlike most conifers, sheds its needles in autumn when the blue-green needles turn to yellow.

Tamarack (*Larix laricina*)

Cross-section of cone seedling

Branchlet with cones

of loose threads, like the ones that grew on the laboratory culture-slides, but with a scattering of algae nodes. And, while lichens don't need soil, they must have something to cling to. They cling by sending out some of the tiny fastidious threads to probe the substrate. The threads can penetrate even between the particles that make up whole rock. Then, as they are alternately wet and dried, a sucker-like mechanical action prises the granules apart, disintegrating the rock and allowing the lichen to insinuate a little farther. In this way the whole surface of the rock is infiltrated for several millimetres; all that shows is a patch of weathering, and the fruiting-bodies.

Other crustose lichens are much larger, and are fully visible, as if the rocks or the tree-trunks had grown a flat spongy scab. What defines the crustose lichens is that they are always firmly attached to their substrate by their entire under-surface, and these larger ones grow in flat patches that cannot be detached except in small fragments. Their thickened cortex, or upper layer, cracks into bluish, greenish, yellow or grey islands, known as *Areolae*, and between these can be seen the black basal layer, called the hypothallus. The algae are dispersed in chains near the light, just under the *Areolae*. In drought such lichens shrink down to a wrinkled papery crust; but after rains the algae sheaths swell and the plant takes on a spongy gelatinous consistency. It may even turn a dull green.

Unlike the crustose lichens, the foliose lichens are only moored here and there to their place of growth, and they develop a protective cortex underneath as well as on top. In fact, some types have only a single central anchor known as an umbilicus. The foliose lichens are more complex than the crustose, for the surface tissue has organized itself into elaborate flat lobes or scaly fronds so that the lichen look ragged and barnacled. (Sometimes, if the lichen growth is particularly luxuriant, and the competition for light is fierce, some of the lobes will begin to rear themselves upright towards the sun.) The most striking of the foliose lichens are the so-called rosette lichens, which form target-like mats on tree-trunks and rocks. They may begin their growth as mere dots on the rock, or on three or four year old twigs, and they grow orbicularly, all round the perimeter, very slowly, until they are a foot or more in diameter.

The foliose lichens are more aggressive than the crustose, and if they get established in the same area, may crowd the crustose ones out. But they in turn are vulnerable to the even more competitive fruticose lichens.

The fruticose lichens have developed the flat lobes and scales into upright sun-seeking stalks and tufts that grow so thickly from their rooting platform that these lichens have a more plant-like look than the other two. They could be some curious sort of moss, at first glance, or perhaps the terrestrial equivalent of an underwater coral or sponge colony. They bear their fruiting-bodies upright as well, and these are often brightly coloured. The familiar little squadrons of British soldiers, with their slender red busbies held erect on slim stalks, belong to this group. So do the so-called reindeer mosses. There are many varieties and hybrids of the reindeer mosses, but they all belong to the species *Cladonia*, and they are the most important and abundant Shield lichens for they are the ground cover of both taiga and tundra; and they are the main fodder of the caribou. Another conspicuous and widespread fruticose lichen on the Shield is old man's beard, of the species *Usnea*. This one grows downward, like Spanish moss, from the rotting bark of old, sick trees. In the south of the Shield, near Lake Superior, the scraggly, wispy tufts of old man's beard are used for nest-material in summer by the parula warblers. But there are beard lichens up near the treeline, too, and in the winter, if the snow is packed too hard over the cladonias on the ground, the dangling tufts overhead make emergency forage for the caribou. For some lichens are edible. They don't contain much protein, and what they do contain is not very digestible, but they have a high carbohydrate content; if they are not very palatable they are at least filling. One kind of rock lichen called *tripe de roche* has been used by Arctic explorers to stave off starvation. Another kind of lichen is even prized as a delicacy in China and Japan. And the "manna" of the Israelites is thought to have been a lichen of a type that becomes detached from its mooring and is wind-blown like tumbleweed across the wastes of Asia Minor. But commercial experiments in making meal of lichens have not been able to overcome the problem of flavour. For lichens secrete a whole range of substances that don't taste very good. A number of them are acids, most very mild, but some strong enough to dissolve old window-glass. It is not clear what role these lichen secretions play. It has been suggested that they help the lichens dissolve the particles of rock where they are establishing themselves. It has been suggested that they are a kind of waterproofing designed to keep the plant's respiration channels open. It has been suggested that they are specifically designed to repel snails, mites and other insects that feed on lichens. And it has been suggested that they are by-products the plant can't get rid of.

Whatever the secretions are for, most of them are coloured – red, orange, yellow, russet – or react chemically to produce colours. Many native people have used lichens as dye-plants, treating them with urine or some other form of ammonia to extract the colour, and boiling them together with materials until the right shade is reached. And the secretions give colour to the lichens themselves. Direct sunlight brings out the brightest, clearest hues, so that lichens tend to be duller-coloured wherever they are in shade, just as they tend to be drabber towards the north of the Shield than in the south. But whether the colours are subtle or brilliant, the lichens are integral to the Shield "look," and part of its definitive vegetation.

In the southern parts of the Shield they are not so conspicuous a part of the landscape, but they are there in surprising variety and brilliance if you know where to look. In the Gatineau, there is a type that spreads only on rocks submerged in the water. The British soldiers can be found marching over rock or sand or the bark of windfalls right up through the mixed-forest playground areas into the boreal forest. In the deeper woods along the north shore of Lake Superior, the wispy tufts of old man's beard hang from the old trees and stir in the wind. Indeed a lichen expert who has travelled extensively throughout the southern parts of the Shield says that he has never seen more kinds of lichen in one place than here along the Superior shore. There are rosette lichens like grey vaccination marks on tree-trunks and twig ends. Whenever the woods are broken by scarps, there are rock tripes on the sheer rock faces. On other outcrops a yellowish crustose variety has spread itself. The yellow is brighter where the outcrops are in sunny clearings. And it is brightest of all – a clear acid yellow – on the top of the rocks, in the direct sunlight. On the sides of the rock away from the sun it shades to a duller, greener yellow. In the same way the British soldiers growing on the sunny sand dunes have yellow stalks: back in the dim woods their stalks were grey. And down along the shore, everywhere, abundantly, there is a foliose lichen on the rocks that achieves a greeny-orange on the side and a rich clear

orange on the topmost surfaces. The most vivid lichens of all, though, are to be found on one or two particular rocks that stand just offshore here. These are bird-rocks, and the thick droppings have attracted specific lichen species that like lime. Most lichens avoid lime, including limestone, but the ones that tolerate it seem to be the most highly coloured of all. These spatter the rocks with sulphur yellow or blazing orange-red. No one knows quite what the mineral requirements or tolerances of lichens are, but where there is a trace of iron in the rock, the lichens growing there will take on a russet colour. Off in Labrador, for example, there is a place where country rock makes a sharp contact with the iron-bearing rock of the Labrador Trough. The junction is as clear in the lichens as it is in the rock, for on one side of the line of contact they are dull brown and beyond it they are a decisive rusty-red.

Here, in this part of Labrador, the lichens are almost the only vegetation to be seen – an endless matted carpet for the rolling rock plain. But they have already begun to take over the landscape back in the great transcontinental belt of conifers, the boreal forest, that covers the vast midsection of the Shield. The transition is gradual. In the heart of the forest, the floor is carpeted in dense, soft feather-mosses. But towards the treeline there begin to be patches of cladonias, the reindeer mosses, here and there. They mark places where the substrate is gravelly, or sandy, or where there is an area of permafrost just below the surface. Closer to the treeline, the permafrost becomes more continuous, and the conditions increasingly arid and subarctic. And now the forest itself begins to change. It is more open and park-like, and the trees are smaller and stunted-looking.

On sandy, well-drained ridges they are apt to be white spruce, but elsewhere they are black spruce, growing no more than twenty or perhaps thirty feet high, in low bushy clumps like rosettes. The spruce are queerly deformed, for their lower branches make elbow-turns upward, so that the main trunk is surrounded by a little thicket of lesser trunks. They look like branched candelabra, and in fact they are known as candelabrum spruce. And the carpet beneath the scattered, stunted trees is wholly of lichens.

This is the taiga, the broad belt of spruce-lichen parkland that forms the transition zone between boreal forest and tundra. It follows the great arc of the treeline across the Shield: indeed the so-called treeline is only an arbitrary device on maps for representing the general limits and trend of this transitional zone.

The lichens that carpet the taiga are mainly cladonias, growing eight or nine inches thick in a continuous spongy ground cover. And it is the cladonias that are deforming the spruce into the candelabrum shape. The fight is for rooting space. The rising lichen cover keeps threatening to cut off the tree from its access to mineral soil. The tree's response is to convert its own lowest branches into suckers. As the rising cover touches and begins to engulf them, the branches put down roots and straighten upwards from this point of contact to make a ring of secondary trunks. As the next lowest set of branches are threatened, they too root downwards and turn upwards.

The struggle takes place in silence and deadly slow motion, for both lichens and spruce grow very slowly here in the sub-arctic. The damage from wildfire may take centuries to repair, and even over-browsing by caribou may set the lichens back for decades. It is here in the taiga that the caribou come to feed in winter, when they can no longer paw through the crust of ice and driven snow out on the tundra. There are swaying black-beard lichens, too, for emergency fodder. And wherever the caribou have packed the snow into hard trails between the trees, yet another species of lichen has established itself, responsive to the slightly different micro-habitat created by the later melting of the packed snow in spring. Because of this, old trails are visible in the lichen woodlands long after the last traveller, man or caribou, has passed.

Here in the taiga the cladonias are dull in colour, varying from pearly-grey to yellowish to brownish-green. When they are dry, they are crackly and brittle underfoot and, since these fragments are all capable of becoming new lichens, it is easy to see how they spread. When they are wet, they will hold up to three times their dry weight in water, and walking in them is like walking in a swamp. But wet or dry, the whole lichen floor of the taiga is cracked into a pattern. It is a mosaic of polygons and it is the beginning of the patterned ground that is so striking a feature of the tundra and the polar desert regions beyond. Out on the tundra, tens of thousands of square miles of low-lying terrain are marked by conspicuous ice-wedge polygons, and frost boils, mud circles and stone rings are common as well. The patterns seem to be caused by underlying permafrost and the peculiar mechanics of frost-heaving in these latitudes. Here in the woodlands the effect is less marked, but nonetheless the cladonia carpet is separated into polygonal tufts, like paving stones. They are easy to detach and lift from the ground and in northern Scandinavia such tufts of edible vegetation are collected in piles near the livestock barns as winter food for reindeer and cattle.

Starting here in the lichen woodlands, these same lichen flag-stones go on to pave the tundra, in patches or continuous cover, all the way to the top edge of the Shield. They are, so far, the unchallenged vegetation of the whole of its northern third. They are the pioneers, and this is their frontier. But they may already be preparing their own downfall. For lichens are peculiarly vulnerable to competition: it is the penalty of specializing – even specializing for poverty. Thus, lichens may invade a field of sand but, as their own remains are added to the soil, other plants come in. In forty years the lichens are severely reduced and in 120 years they have virtually disappeared. Lichens have already been displaced by ranker vegetation on all the better sites in the south of the Shield. And the feather mosses seem to be advancing on them in the boreal forest. And in a way they have brought it on themselves.

For, even out on the tundra they are preparing the way for other plants. Their own dry, dead filaments, and the cast-off portions of the thallus, together with rock dust and bird droppings and fine organic debris, get blown on the wind to lodge in rock cracks or against the growing lichen mats themselves. And thus a filling is formed in which other species can come and root. And the lichens will yield to them because, from the very beginning, the partnership was formed not in order to fight but in order to escape.

Lichens, by the way, are vulnerable to one other threat besides competition. They are very efficient at secreting substances, but they do not seem able to excrete them. Thus they retain the lichen acids. And thus, too, they have been found to build up extraordinary concentrations of strontium-90 and other radioactive fallout products. The fallout doesn't kill them – but the polluted smokes and gases and other waste products of man's civilization do. Lichens may specialize in living where no other plant in nature can, but no lichens grow in cities.

13 A SEA OF MUSKEG

People who try to describe the Shield in any sort of perspective keep coming back to the view from the air. Only the aerial view makes it clear how monolithic a unit this is. And yet, perversely, only the aerial view makes clear the variety within the monotony.

There are several strong imprints on the Shield. One is the structure and grain of the Precambrian bedrock. Another is the mark of the glaciers – both the glacial gouging and the eccentric forms of glacial debris. A third is the pattern of running and standing water. The climate is still another imprint, imposing certain broad vegetational zones from south to north – mixed forest, taiga, tundra – as well as local conditions such as rainfall and the presence of permafrost. The bold general patterns are superimposed one upon another across the whole face of the Shield.

The vegetation itself is the final overlay. It is, comparatively speaking, a simple flora. In the language of one botanist, "the country is almost entirely occupied by aggressive, wide-ranging ecologically undemanding species." Which is to say that, given an event as recent and as total as glaciation, the landscape is dominated by the comparatively few plant types that are good pioneers – cold-hardy, fast-moving and not too finicky. The lichens are superb pioneers. The conifers are pretty good, too, and so are some deciduous weed-trees like poplars and willows and alders, and some of the heath plants and the mosses.

But here too there is variety within monotony. For, like the lichens, each species within the various families has its own habitat preferences, its own weaknesses and its own tolerances. And so the vegetation expresses with stunning fidelity every nuance of the interplay between climate and landform. At the treeline, the fingers and islands of spruce that persist on to the tundra represent favourable habitats, perhaps with a southern exposure. There is white spruce on the good, well-drained ridges, but stunted black candelabrum spruce on the poor ground. In the forest belt, the bottom lands along the streams are covered with thickets of willows and alders. But where there is sandy glacial outwash, there is jack pine.

This is the sort of thing that can be seen from the air: a bold, piebald pattern of plant distributions, concentrations and absences that map in technicolour the physical conditions in every part of the Shield. Providing, that is, they are seen with a knowing eye.

To anyone who has flown over the Shield, one of the striking sights is the muskeg. Canada has more muskeg – 500,000 square miles – than any other country in the world. Most of it, though not all, is on the Shield, within the limits of the boreal forest zone. It is widespread here because the right conditions coincide repeatedly within this zone of the Shield: a cold but not Arctic climate, a low, gently rolling relief, more precipitation in the year than the land can get rid of, and the availability of sphagnum moss, the muskeg-forming plant. For absorbency, sphagnum is the next best thing to a sponge.

And so, repeatedly, the boreal forest is interrupted by great open expanses of waterland. These are not swamps, which are simply low-lying areas of forest flooded with sluggishly moving water. Such spruce swamps are common, but they are scarcely visible through the spruce canopy, and they are not muskeg. The muskeg, in contrast, is as visible as an oil slick, and it has the smeary pastel patterns of an oil slick, too. The sun glints off a thousand small pools and ribbons of water that seem to converge on the horizon into broad sheets and splashes of dull pewter. These are cells of standing water, held within a spongy maze of hummocks. The hummocks are a tawny colour, picked out with the decadent apple-green of bog plants seen from the air. There are trees, but they are islanded into occasional dark-green strips and splotches. In places there are low, swelling spruce-ringed whalebacks, as well, bald in the centre. The sodden blotchy terrain can go on for miles. The most astonishing stretch occurs on the sediments of the Hudson Bay lowlands. A continuous sea of muskeg occupies the flats for about eight hundred miles, from the Nottaway and Harricanaw Rivers of Quebec around James Bay and up to Churchill, Manitoba. At its broadest, along the Albany River, this swathe is some two hundred miles wide. But muskeg occurs everywhere on the Shield gneisses too. And repeatedly its pattern steadies into rhythms that cannot help catching the eye. Often the hummocks are elongated into wavering strings so that, with the water lying between them, the ground looks tiger-striped. In other places the water looks as if it had collected in a series of pockmarks. Sometimes the spruce-islands occur in flotillas athwart the pattern, like minnows poised in a current. And mile after mile of the lowlands muskeg is marshalled into fine corrugations, like ripples in packed sand.

It is one thing to see these patterns from the air. It is another thing entirely to interpret them. For on the ground muskeg makes appalling country to try to get around in. Parts of the Hudson Bay Railway to Churchill, Manitoba, keep sinking into it. At its worst it can even swallow the special muskeg tractors. And an investigator on foot doesn't get very far; even if he keeps to the quaking, squishy tops of the hummocks, he is repeatedly detoured by bog pools. This is black fly country, too.

So it is scarcely surprising that until very recently not much muskeg research went on in the heart of the Shield. It was easier to assume that Shield muskeg was the same, or very nearly the same, as the smaller bogs handy to the research centres. These bogs had been well studied, and an elegant and detailed model of bog formation had been worked out. It seemed to fit the known circumstances: that bogs had a continuous tussocky cover of living sphagnum moss; that the sphagnum made the bog-water acid, and hard on other plants, so that only a few acid-tolerant species – leatherleaf, the heath plants like Labrador tea and cranberry, and perhaps, finally, black spruce – could move in; and that bogs were uncommonly good at forming peat. Peat simply means any soggy organic material that isn't fully rotted. It is normally an intermediate stage between raw humus and proper soil. But the point about the peat in bogs is that it never does rot fully. The water in bogs is cut off from wind and wave action so all its oxygen is quickly used up. And, being acid, the water repels most bacteria. So the two most important agents of rot, oxygen and bacteria, don't get a chance, and the peat simply

Bogs are characterized by large peat deposits, floating sedge, heath shrubs, like cranberry and leatherleaf, and the coniferous black spruce.

goes on and on building up.

The model of bog formation worked out by the investigators began with blocked drainage: a pond or lake cut off from its outlet. Then a succession of plants that liked stagnant water would move in: rushes and sedges round the edge, aquatic plants with creeping stems and floating leaves, like the pondweeds, out along the bottom from the shore. The pond would get more and more choked with growth, and also with a build-up of dead plant remains. These particular plants are inclined to produce acid remains, and eventually the acid would build up sufficiently for the sphagnum to creep out along the floating mat of vegetation and bridge the pond. Sphagnum needs acid water.

It is impossible to understand bogs or muskeg without understanding sphagnum. Up to ninety per cent of the bog mass is sphagnum, or peat composed of sphagnum remains. And sphagnum keeps creating those conditions that it needs itself and that perpetuate and even increase the bog. After a while, almost nothing but sphagnums can grow there.

Sphagnums are a family of mosses and, like the rest, they can reproduce either sexually or vegetatively. Vegetative reproduction is very useful when conditions are rough, and it is usually the sign of an exceptionally hardy plant.

But what distinguishes sphagnums from other mosses is the very peculiar structure of the leaves. They are like thin sections of cellulose foam – a mesh of large dead cells alternating with tiny living ones. The dead cells are empty and perforated, and thus they can soak up and hold water. Sphagnum, then, is what makes the bog a sponge.

It establishes itself in a thick, floating mat of sod across the pond. The upper parts grow on from year to year, but as the lower parts die and disintegrate, the bits sink through the water to add to the growing layer of peat. At this point the bog in the classic model has a quaking surface of sphagnum, a thick layer of muck on the bottom, and a layer of water between. Perhaps a few of the specialized heath plants have found a solid footing on the sphagnum as well.

Pond bogs in this condition can be found close to most of the settled parts of Canada, and there are thousands on the Shield. They can be found in the earlier, sedge-choked, formative stages as well.

And they can be found in later stages, too. For bog forma-tion, according to the model, is a perfect illustration of the long-held belief among botanists and ecologists that in a pioneer habitat the plant types progress from the simpler to the more complex until a stable community has evolved. The evolution is called "succession," and the stable community is called a "climax." Sedges and rushes, sphagnums and heath plants are all primitive plants. Obviously they had eventually to be replaced by some higher form. In this view, just as it is the fate of a lake to be siphoned off, it is the fate of a bog to become dry land. So in time the floating sphagnum mat grounds on the rising peat bottom and there is no more water layer; with this firm footing the sphagnum grows above the level of the water table. And finally – though perhaps not without a setback or two – the bog has become a dry peat bed, solid enough to support black spruce.

There's only one difficulty with the model: it explains most small bogs, including a great number on the Shield; but it doesn't at all explain the muskeg of the boreal and subarctic regions. The difficulty might have suggested itself a long time ago, if air travel had been commoner. Pond-filled bogs are almost by definition smallish bodies shaped like ponds. The Shield muskegs are great regional bogs and fens whose perimeters are hard to trace and whose strange linear patterns find no explanation in the successional story. From time to time a visiting ecologist, perhaps one who had worked in Scandinavia or north Germany, suggested he recognized some of the patterns. But the classic bog formation model, which is the one in all the textbooks, seems to have created a sort of mental block. As one bog ecologist put it recently, "Many of us find it difficult to conceive of other possibilities."

The evidence that the muskeg is a different breed of bog has really only been accumulating for the last decade. So far, few studies have been done and there is much that is not known. But enough has been pieced together, eked out with work in northern Europe, to construct at least a model. This is how the new model for bogs in a cold climate goes.

These are peatlands – for which the Indian word is muskeg. Some of them, including the great stretch in the Hudson Bay lowlands, are properly described as fens. This simply means that instead of being strongly acid, the water in them still contains some minerals, some nutrients and some oxygen. In turn, this

HUNTERS ON THE WING

Hunting year round in the boreal forest of the Shield, the carnivorous owls doze by day and strike silently by night. They prey on mice and rabbits, as does this small saw-whet owl. Hunters of different prey invade every spring, and the forest awakens to the tumultuous sound of millions of warblers, who arrive to feast on the newly-hatched insects.

Equipped to kill

As predatory birds of the northern forest, owls are superbly equipped to be master hunters. With sharp powerful talons and a compact, hooked beak that is designed for chopping and ripping, the owl plunges silently down upon its prey, which may be a rabbit or a snake even larger than the owl itself. Nocturnal hunting is aided by the great light-gathering power of the owl's binocular eyes, and the remarkable sensitivity of the long, asymmetrical slits that are its ears. The ear-slits are well hidden behind the facial disc, and although some owls appear to have ears on top of their heads, these are merely tufts of feathers. In total darkness with no light penetration, owls can see no better than other animals, but by using hearing alone are able to zero in on their prey with amazing accuracy. However, birds of prey are not creatures of pure destruction. Because their victims are mostly the weak and unfit, predators help to preserve the vitality of their prey and are necessary to the health of the wildlife community.

1. With the speed of a hawk, and the silent flight of an owl, the hawk-owl is a daytime hunter in the muskeg of the far north, where summer nights are short.

2. The most powerful of all, the great horned owl is formidable in the defense of its nest. It breeds early in the year and incubates eggs while snow lies all around.

3. The great gray owl is thickly feathered, and not as fearsome as its size suggests. It can be frequently seen in winter, forced into populated areas to search for food.

4. The boreal owl is a particularly effective hunter. This one has carried its prey to a concealed branch, and warns off intruders with a yellow-eyed stare.

Feeding the young

Every summer, the woodlands of the Shield welcome the activity of more than 200 pairs of birds per 100 acres, migrants that move in coincidental with the spring hatching of myriad insect larvae. Over half the summer population consists of tiny warblers, hyper-active and vividly coloured, arriving in waves from tropical climes to seek out breeding places. An individual niche is necessary for successful breeding, and the woods are full of warning songs and calls proclaiming territory. Digestion is continuous and warblers must feed on insects many times a day, the fluttering activity doubling when the young are born. As early as mid-August, the warblers begin to head for more southern climates. By the end of summer, their bright dress changed to drab, 700 million warblers have left the boreal forest.

1. A very handsome and active bird, the American redstart builds a firm nest of grasses and bits of bark, amongst a group of upright branches, 6 to 25 feet up.

2. A loose, fragile nest of twigs and fine grasses is made by the rose-breasted grosbeak. In this species, both sexes sing, which is an unusual phenomenon among birds.

3. The unmistakable scarlet tanager builds its loose, rather shallow nest well out on a horizontal branch of a tree, anywhere from ten to fifty feet above ground.

4. The chestnut-sided warbler nests close to the ground usually in a low bush. Three to five spotted white eggs are incubated in a nest made of bark and weed stalks.

5. Nesting in a cavity excavated by other birds in a living or dead tree, the hairy woodpecker forages from bottom to top of the tree, hunting for grubs to feed its young.

5

Sphagnum moss

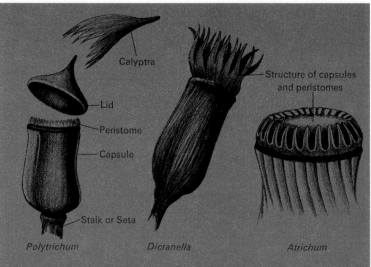

Calyptra

Lid

Peristome

Capsule

Stalk or Seta

Structure of capsules
and peristomes

Polytrichum   *Dicranella*   *Atrichum*

Many mosses are difficult to identify, and several distinguishing features are used. The number and form of teeth around the capsule opening (peristome) are important in identification, and other features used are the size and shape of the capsule, the length of stalk (seta), and structure of leaves.

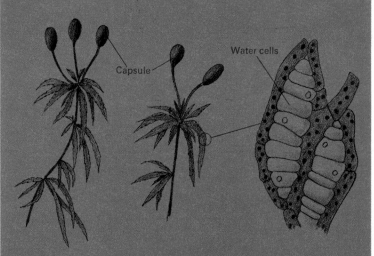

Capsule

Water cells

Like the spoon-leaved sphagnum above, all peat-mosses have two kinds of leaf cells: food-building cells, and water-retaining cells. Sphagnum is extremely absorbent due to the storage capacity of the water cells, and grows in great masses in bogs, where it swells and diminishes the area of open water.

usually means there is some water flow through the fen, even if the flow is sluggish. So instead of sphagnums invading, wholesale, the sedges and rushes can keep renewing themselves. The reasons for the widespread ripply pattern are not very well understood, yet, except that it seems to have something to do with the whole mysterious subject of hydraulics. In some way, the sluggish water distributes the silt and organic material into furrows, packing the solids into parallel ridges of peat separated by soggy ditches. There may be random patches of spruce in the fen, wherever the peat is thin enough for the trees to get roots down to mineral soil. The spruce are usually candelabrum spruce, deformed by the fight to stay in touch with nutrients.

But the typical boreal zone peatland is not a fen but a raised bog. Raised bogs are known in north Germany, where they are called high-mires, and in Siberia and the British Isles as well. Their characteristic is to be swollen into a low dome like bread that has been set to rise. In the aerial view of the muskeg, the spruce-ringed whalebacks that seemed threadbare on top were not hills but small raised bogs. The sphagnum was far too thick in the centre for any spruce to get its roots down. What's more, it seems unlikely that spruce will ever grow on top of the dome, which makes this bog a far cry from the pond-bog with its inevitable succession towards dry land.

Furthermore, the raised bogs get their start not in any deep catch-basin but on flat ground or, even more commonly, on a very gentle gradient, perhaps only six feet in a mile.

What tips the scales and starts a raised bog (or a fen, which also gets started on flat or sloping ground) is a high P/E ratio: more precipitation than evaporation. In theory, an excessive P/E ratio could happen anywhere, but in practice it happens almost entirely in the boreal zone, where the average annual rain- and snowfall may be light but the thin sun in the short summers never really burns off the surplus. The boreal zone averages 40″ of precipitation a year at best (and twelve to twenty inches at worst) but so little evaporates that its climate is effectively moist, and a good deal of low ground is waterlogged all year round. (The tundra gets so little precipitation that the problem doesn't arise; there are no bogs on the tundra.) The surplus water, with nowhere else to go, stands on the surface, or perhaps seeps imperceptibly downhill. Sodden mineral soil is just what sedges like. The sedges and bulrushes and horsetails begin to grow. If the surplus of water is never very great, they will settle in permanently. Their remains will form a thick black mucky peat in which each new generation will root itself. The percolation of run-off water will bring just enough nutrients from elsewhere to feed them and in time it will begin to pattern the peat according to its own laws, and perhaps according to the laws of freezing and thaw. The mildly supersaturated ground will remain a fen.

But if there is a bigger surplus of water, and if there is any slope to the ground at all, the slow seepage of water will be backed-up and trapped, upslope, where it first encounters the sedge growth. A puddle of standing water will start to spread there, gradually taking on an acid tinge from the sedge remains. And standing water, of course, is just what the sphagnum likes.

The sphagnum moves into this upslope position, and from then on it soaks up all the percolating water, like the sponge it is. The sedges downslope are cut off from the nutrients of the run-off and soon the luxuriating sphagnum has overgrown them. (Drill-cores of old raised bogs always show a layer of sedge peat as the base for the sphagnum peat.) The sphagnum encroaches uphill as well, blocking the water ever higher up the slope and moving in to take advantage of it. This spreading by what it feeds on is called "paludification" which simply means swamping. If the slope has been forested, the sphagnum will undermine and fell trees whose rotting wood becomes part of the peat. The wood rots only until it is buried. Whatever is below the skin of a bog is cut off from oxygen and bacteria. Plant remains do not decompose for centuries.

At this point a very important stage in raised bog formation is reached. Sphagnum's absorbency is so great that it draws ground-water upwards, thus permitting still more of the moss to grow on top. It can thus raise itself a bit above ground level and the water table even in normal climates. But here it doesn't matter if it is cut off from the water table. Here, by definition, there is more precipitation than evaporation. The sphagnum can thrive on the precipitation alone, soaking it up and using it for growth as necessary. It begins to swell upwards like a great pudding. How high it can grow depends precisely on the P/E ratio: the greater the surplus the higher it grows. There are mechanical limits to height, of course – though ocean-damp Ireland has some abnormally steep bogs formed on hillsides that are held

together entirely by surface vegetation. In historic times there was a slight increase in rainfall which turned out to be the last straw for one bog: it burst and the peat poured over the countryside like foul black gruel.

Eventually the bog reaches its maximum size and the bog process halts. The water at its surface is simply rainwater, poor in minerals and bases. The bog plants growing there are those that can stand being starved for lime, phosphorus and nitrogen. Unless there is a climate change, it can remain permanently just as it is: a great peat haggis. Some living bogs are thousands of years old.

On the other hand, something else can happen. No one knows why it happens, except that it is common closer to the treeline and probably has something to do with increased cold. Whatever sets the pattern up, it is probably maintained and emphasized by frost action and by gravity creep of the peat. In any case, the skin of the raised bog develops little rips. The rips form in the pattern of ripples widening from the centre of the dome, except that at any given level downslope they are interrupted slits rather than a continuous ring. Some bogs where this has happened on the Shield have been examined, and it appears that the slits developed simultaneously about three thousand years ago. Water gradually percolates into the rips so that they form stepped catchment-basins down the slope. The sphagnum between them remains high, however, and crowned with its bog plants. From the air the gentle gradient from dome to perimeter flattens out, and what can be seen are the little regularly spaced water-filled dimples between the sphagnum hummocks. In many of these bogs, though, the dimples join up to become ribbons and streaks of water separated by strips of sphagnum. This is the pattern that looks tiger-striped from the air and it is also the pattern that gives these bogs their name. They are called string-bogs. The water-filled rips are called *flarks*.

There is another strong pattern in the string bogs, and for this one there is scarcely even the beginning of an explanation. In places there are flotillas of spruce islands, teardrop-shaped, heading up the slopes with their tails trailing downslope. They are, that is to say, at right angles to the string pattern of the bog. Some investigators think the answer may lie in the peculiar hydraulics of sluggishly percolating water in response to different densities and resistances in the peat. In any case the islands are obviously dry enough, and the sphagnum on them is sufficiently thin, for the spruce to root.

There is another kind of patterned bog that occurs closest of all to the treeline. It is called a palsa bog, and it is simply the condition that overtakes a raised bog in the permafrost zone: plugs of frozen sphagnum-capped peat raise themselves above the general level of the bog like frozen milk forcing up the cap on a milk bottle. These, too, may dry out sufficiently for the black spruce to establish themselves, making another sort of spruce-island design. Beyond the treeline, on the tundra, the bogs disappear: instead there are the polygon lichen-turfs and patterned ground of intensive frost action.

The granite gneisses of the Shield help to foster raised bog formation, for they make acid soils that encourage the sphagnum at the outset. (The fens in the Hudson Bay lowlands persist partly because they are on marine sediments, which keep feeding nutrients to the ground-water.) And the Shield terrain, with its long dip-slopes and gentle domes, provides ideal contours. In fact neighbouring bogs, spreading upslope and down, can easily grow together. The union will provide a variety of marginal conditions and – as is the way with the Shield – the vegetation will map these too. Where a trickle of mineralized ground-water can manage to force a way, sedges will move in anew. And tamaracks may find enough soil to move in after them. But where there is a fen with dead trees standing in it, the sphagnum is advancing: the trees have lost their mineral contact and the fen is on its way to becoming a raised bog.

In places there are – even in these strange subarctic bogs – tropical flowers. In the wettest sites there are pitcher-plants. Sogginess and nitrogen deficiency are common to rain forests as well as northern bogs, and in the tropics the pitcher-plant learned to get its nutrients by drowning and digesting insects in its throat. So the pitcher-plant has been able to make its way into the patterned bogs of the Shield. The orchids (like the heath plants) have solved the same problem by teaming up with nitrogen-fixing fungi, whose threads entwine their roots. So a few of the hardier orchids can sometimes be found by those who are minded to go into the muskeg on foot to look.

The pitcher plant *feeds on bodies of small insects which become trapped by the stiff downward-pointing hairs on the nectared sides of the trap-leaf. Some mosquito larvae (right) however, are able to survive and live off bacteria and algae inside the otherwise deadly plant.*

14 THE BOREAL LANDSCAPE

Boreal forest crosses the Shield from the far northwest to the Labrador coast in a great broad swag that averages six hundred miles in width. Along its northern edge it grades through the increasingly open lichen woodland of the taiga into the lichen heath and patterned ground of the tundra. Even beyond the treeline, occasional clumps of trees may occupy a good protected site. But the trees are apt to be stunted, and deformed by wind-and-ice-blast. There are dwarf willows scarcely a foot high growing from cracks in the rock, and bent crabbed little black spruce creeping like gorse through a gully. Anywhere close to the treeline, growth is so slow that a tree standing no more than five feet high may be a hundred years old; its annual growth rings will be so fine as to be almost indistinguishable.

To the south, along the southern margins of the Shield, the boreal forest grades either into the open aspen parkland of the Prairies or into the fine painterly forest of the Great Lakes-St. Lawrence zone, with its upstanding pines and hemlocks, and its maples blazoned against the dark hills in spectacular beauty in the fall.

Between these two transitional zones, the conifers have their domain. Boundaries are hard to draw, but one estimate of the boreal forest area is a million and a quarter square miles. To anyone used to the bourgeois, dishevelled landscapes of human settlement, the boreal forest is impressive in its sameness. Right across the continent, broken only by the lakes and streams, by muskeg on the low ground and by the outcrops of bare rock, there is the same dark evergreen ground-mass, the same steepled skyline. It has been called "the typical Canadian landscape."

There are no more than a dozen important tree species in all the forest. There are the deciduous weed-trees of the river edges, burn-clearings and cut-over areas: the birch, the alder, the willow and the poplar. There is the foamy, feathering tamarack (or larch, or hackmatack) of the fens and peatlands, turning yellow in the fall before it drops its needles. There is the jack pine, with its antique look, stiff and heavy, like a tree on an oriental screen. The jack pine has a touch of the oriental asceticism too: it will grow from a granite cleft where there seems to be no soil for its roots, and it will grow in poor sandy plains too porous to hold much groundwater.

All these trees are widespread, occurring singly or in stands throughout most of the forest. But they are mere incidentals to the three conifers that are its very fabric: the white spruce, the black spruce, and the balsam fir. These are the three trees whose seemingly endless repetition appalls the wayfarer.

If there were a folklore about them, the white spruce and the black spruce would be brothers, but the white spruce would be the favoured one, the darling. It grows fair and straight and tall, assuming the good ground as its natural right. It grows wherever there are well-drained ridges, and good mineral nutriments, and perhaps a bit of lime-rich marine shale instead of the poor, acid soil that granites make. This is true throughout the forest, but the central and western part is where the white spruce comes into its heritage and grows most thickly and well. Spruce-pine-aspen is the typical mixed forest of the western Shield.

The black spruce would be the dark discontented one, smaller and cleverer than his brother, left to shift for himself but full of guile and not ever to be underestimated. This is the black spruce that borders muskeg and the swamp, and wrestles silently with the rising tide of lichens in the lichen woodlands. And it holds sway along all the northern marches of forest. Yet it is an odd thing that where conditions are most extreme the black spruce creeps cunningly low to the ground; but there are often outposts of white spruce in the same area, or even beyond and, though the trees may be dwarfed and no more than a foot or so high, they still have the proud habit of trees and grow upright. The balsam fir is a handsome and demanding eastern consort for the white spruce. From the Atlantic across the Shield as far as Prince Albert National Park in Saskatchewan, the white spruce and balsam fir commonly occur in stands on the richer soil together. Fir-spruce is the typical forest of the east.

A third of the surface of Canada is forested with these few tree species – and yet to the specialist's eye the forest has variety and drama and flux, and as many moods as there are combinations and permutations of the trees. In one standard reference, the boreal forest is subdivided into thirty-three types.

Along the forested margins of the Shield in the prairie provinces, for example, pure groves of second-growth aspen can

be found, and these have an atmosphere of their own. Aspens have slim, smooth trunks that can rise almost sixty feet before they are crowned with foliage. Even if the trees are close enough together so that the overhead canopy is continuous, the grove will still be sunny and light-dappled. Between the crown and the forest floor there will be two more layers of vegetation. At waist height, shrubs such as red raspberry and dogwood make a thick understory. And then, rooted in the good moist compost of rotting poplar leaves, mosses and herbs such as twin-flower and wintergreen carpet the ground. Springtails and mites and other soil insects busily mine the compost. Here and there a staunch little white spruce seedling from a windborne seed may push up among the herbs. But there are few aspen saplings for, unlike the spruce, they need light to start growing, and not enough can penetrate the understory of shrubs.

A pure stand of white spruce in the heart of the boreal forest is quite different to this – cool and dim as a church. These trees, too, grow to eighty feet or more, but the bushy boughs, massed in a narrow helix from ground to spire, blot out both light and heat. The air is resinous and still, heavy with the smell of Christmas. There is no understory at all, but underfoot the ground is springy with a smooth turf of moss and dead needles. Nothing else but the moss seems able to grow here, except where a tree has fallen and left a gap in the canopy overhead. For, like the sphagnum in bogs, the spruce itself makes this environment difficult. Conifers help create podsol. The carpet of needle litter, called duff, is strongly acid in composition. Water seeping through the moss layer into the ground carries the acid with it, and this dissolves and leaches away essential nutrients just at the level where most plants would root.

This impoverished horizon just under the humus is the sign of podsol; it shows up as a poor-looking, ashy-grey layer hostile even to earthworms. The spruce itself can stand the acid-rich, nutrient-poor conditions it creates, though most other

Although the Canadian Shield has been scraped clean by the last glacial advance and retreat, a thin covering of moss and other shallow rooted plants has returned to the area. Gradually, as these plants die and the base rock erodes, a new and deep soil layer will begin to cover the Shield permitting the growth of more deeply rooted plants. Eventually, trees will return to areas now covered by solid rock.

vegetation can't. But even the spruce has trouble seeding here, for the continuous moss layer, growing on a pallid nest of its own dead underparts, is too thick. Any white spruce seedlings to be found are usually rooted in the rich punky wood of a windfall – though they may also get a footing in the raw earth where the windfall was uprooted. Even if they have got established they face hazards. A young plant makes tender browse for the varying hare or, in winter, for the moose. A white spruce stand is the resort of much animal life. Here and there, near the bases of the trees, red squirrels have dropped piles of spruce-cone scales. And warblers and kinglets weave busily in and out among the blue-green needles harvesting grubs and larvae.

A black spruce forest is quite different, even at the same latitudes. Along the Labrador coast, for example, there is a scrub forest of dwarfed black spruce and balsam fir so dense and thickety that a man can't push his way through. And farther north, in fact throughout the whole northern part of the boreal forest, the black spruce produce a still more sinister ambience. This black spruce forest of the subarctic seems a dark, ancient vegetable place, dripping with moisture. Thick feather mosses carpet the floor as they do in the white spruce stands farther south, but here they are soggy and lush, shrouding stones and fallen trunks, filling in small depressions, muffling any footfall. Black beard lichen sway from the branches and there are scabs of lichen on all the twig-tips. The trees grow in clumps, some as much as two hundred years old and soft with rot. The smell is of punk and fungus.

As this forest grades northward the trees are progressively smaller and slower-growing. The tallest black spruce in the forest may be no more than forty-two feet, and a foot-high seedling may already be eighteen years old. With such a growth rate, the rising moss cover is a constant threat, and the black spruce respond in the same way as they do in the spruce-lichen taiga at the treeline. The bottom branches that are being overtaken by moss put down roots where they brush the ground and then turn upward from the point of contact. The result is the candelabrum shape, and adaptation for sheer survival. One such candelabrum spruce, found in an Ungava forest, was rooted only a foot into the soil but had thirty-seven stems. The tallest stem was only twenty-three feet high, though the tree was ninety years old.

The black spruce

Black Spruce
30 to 40 feet

Cone scale with seeds

Single seed

Cones
0.5 to 1 inch long

Black spruce, Canada's most northerly growing tree, exists in favourable patches on the tundra north of the treeline which has to be regarded less as a line than as a zone between forest and tundra.

This black spruce feather-moss forest is very widespread and characteristic in the north, and perpetuates the meanest, sourest podsols of all. And nothing likes to feed on the acid, tough spruce needles. Even the voracious budworm larvae eat black spruce foliage only as third-best after the white spruce and balsam fir. Indeed animal life seems to go out of its way to avoid the black spruce feather-moss forest, with its damp exhalations and its muffled silence. As one impressed botanist wrote, "The peace of death hangs over this forest."

Because the black spruce is left to occupy the poorer, ill-drained land, it is often marginal to great stretches of muskeg. Between the two there is commonly a curious transition zone where the spruce are scattered on isolated small mounds of podsol surrounded by wet sphagnum peatland. This zone has its own specific association of plants, common neither to adjoining forest nor adjoining muskeg. Then, right along the margins of the muskeg will be the familiar "forest of sticks," where the black spruce have already been swamped.

At the northern limits of the black spruce feather-moss forest another sort of transition occurs. Here it grades into the parkland of the taiga. The candelabrum spruce grow more and more widely spaced, and more dwarfed and clumpy. And the turf of feathermoss yields to the polygon tussocks of cladonia that begin here and stretch off to the north across the tundra. It is as though some threshold of tolerance for boreal forest vegetation had been reached.

And yet there are places where feather-moss can be found growing under and among disintegrating lichens, very much as though the mosses were still on the move north, and were invading.

And there are the spruce themselves, both black and white, and the dwarf willows and alders, stubbornly creeping from one favourable site to the next north of the treeline. But, curiously, there is evidence of retreat as well. Radio-carbon research makes it clear that the tundra just beyond the treeline was forested for long enough, some time in the past, for podsols to develop. In fact the treeline has advanced north of its present location at least twice since the last Ice Age – and it withdrew far to the south between the two advances. The treeline clearly has to be regarded as an unstable boundary, open to revision through natural means. In any case it is less a clearcut frontier than a mosaic of forest-and-tundra patches.

Indeed all through the boreal forest, in spite of its seeming monotony, the expert sees not just variety but flux. A few years ago an African ecologist joined a botanical excursion through part of the taiga. Afterwards he wrote, "Compared with the African forest and savannah, the Boreal Forest appears an entire newcomer to the world scene."

And that is what it is: a newcomer. Not even a hundred tree-generations have passed since the ice-denuded moraines and bedrock were first colonized by plants. And the vegetation has had great distances to travel: it is pretty well agreed that the plants and animals from the northern half of the continent crowded south and west ahead of the glaciers and waited out the last Ice Age either in the southern United States or in the unglaciated sections of the Yukon and Alaska. As the glaciers withdrew, stock from these refuges moved back to repopulate the raw land. The first reinvasion could only have involved such desperate opportunists as the lichens. In fact something very like a narrow and impermanent tundra zone must have followed close behind the retreating ice. But other enterprising vegetation must have been, so to speak, hard on its heels.

All species that dominate the forest today are fast travellers, with light windborne or waterborne seed. Spruce that now occupy the Keewatin District, for example, are more than a thousand miles from any possible Ice Age refuge. They must have started early and advanced themselves three or four miles in every generation in order to cover the distance in the elapsed time.

A rough logic governs present dispersal of the dominants throughout the forest. The white spruce grows on the best ground. The balsam fir needs rather more moisture than the white pruce in order to flourish and grows best in the east where precipitation is greater. Both the tamarack and the jack pine are very adaptable but not very competitive, so they content themselves with the sites despised by the others – sand for the jack pine, fens for the tamarack. The resourceful and devious black spruce, unique to North American forest, has made an even more successful specialty of the strenuous sites – and maintains its edge by degrading the habitat past the tolerance of almost any tree competitor. But no species, not even the black spruce, has anything more than squatters' rights. The boreal

forest hasn't even begun to stabilize yet – if indeed it is meant to.

A silent, ferocious battle for ascendancy goes on without let-up. The white spruce tries to overwhelm competition with sheer fecundity. It gives off so much pollen that the discharge is sometimes visible as a cloud over the forest, and pollen can be scooped up by the handful from the surface of a forest lake. (In Sweden spruce forests have been estimated to produce 75,000 tons of pollen a year.) And when the pollen has fertilized the cones and the cones have ripened, as many as 400,000 seeds may be released on a single acre. That's in a good year. The conifers have flowering rhythms, but in the North American taiga these seem to get broken or forced occasionally into cone-crop peaks followed by years when no cones at all are produced.

The balsam fir counters by having a larger seed that develops into a bushier, healthier seedling in the critical first year of growth. As an added advantage, the balsam fir begins reproduction somewhere around its twentieth year, while the white spruce remains infertile till it is fifty or sixty years old. In the right circumstances, then, the balsam fir can take over what started as a mixed white spruce-balsam fir forest. In the Lac Seul area of northwestern Ontario, for example, the spruce in one such forest decreased by sixteen per cent in twenty-two years, while the fir increased by 366 per cent.

Yet the white spruce can still retaliate. The balsam fir doesn't live much past sixty, while the white spruce may last two hundred years or more. As long as it keeps a foothold in the forest it still has a chance to repossess the site.

If time is on the side of the white spruce, opportunism is on the side of the hardwoods. Even given unlimited fecundity, white spruce reproduction still hangs on one seed's finding itself a rooting spot, and escaping many subsequent perils. In a mixed forest, the leaves that fall in autumn may be enough to smother a tiny spruce seedling. Rodents or hares may eat it. A late frost in the spring may kill it off. And while it struggles to survive, the hardwoods may already have moved in, crowding its roots and cutting it off from light. For the hardwoods have the useful knack of reproducing vegetatively as well as sexually. The aspen, for example, sprouts from the roots, and its root system is widespread; a few large trees can produce enough suckers to populate an acre of ground.

And yet the opportunist hardwoods, too, are vulnerable.

Unlike the conifers, they are not shade-tolerant; the suckers will die off after a few years if they are cut off from light. The hardwoods simply cannot reproduce themselves where there is any dense understory of shrubs, let alone a closed canopy of tree crowns. So a stand of aspen or birch in a cut-over area may flare up and grow to maturity but it cannot perpetuate itself past one generation.

The black spruce, with its candelabrum form, can resort to vegetative reproduction when threatened, too; and being shade-tolerant, it can also keep seeding itself in its own shadow. Add to this its habitat-fouling characteristic and it might seem that, once established, nothing could oust it. Occasionally an invader will try; a windfall will leave an open space in the spruce-moss forest and before any black spruce seedlings have time to take hold, the aggressive heath plants such as Labrador tea or snowberry root themselves and begin to spread. But there is no hospitality here. Though the shrubs may flower and fruit for a while, eventually they grow sterile and cede their position. Nor can the white spruce or the balsam fir get a foothold; they require a higher standard of living.

According to ecological theory, more tough and successful species keep replacing the simpler pioneering species until a perfect match with the environment is reached, in which the so-called "climax" vegetation is self-perpetuating. The succession leading to black spruce might, for example, have started with tamarack yielding to balsam fir; or it might have started with a mixed aspen-white spruce forest in which the white spruce shaded out the aspens and then were invaded by black spruce seedlings when a series of untimely frosts killed off their own vulnerable offspring. In any case, one widely quoted boreal forest expert has observed, "If there are any such things as climax forests in nature, the spruce-feather-moss forest is certainly one of them." The black spruce forest seems more changeless and entrenched the older it grows.

And yet here too permanence is only an appearance. For the slow-motion struggle with the mosses for rooting space goes on continuously. The sodden muskeg continues its pre-emptive creep up the slope towards the margins. There is rot inside the tree trunks and fungus on the branches. A tree falls, and then another and another. When there are enough gaps, the subarctic winds have a clear sweep. And where the wind can get at them, trees so shallowly anchored as the black spruce stand little chance against wholesale uprooting. The gaps grow wider and the forest begins to disintegrate. What would happen next? Perhaps Labrador tea and the snowberry would try again. Perhaps the muskeg would seize its chance and claim the site. If the site were an exposed slope, drought caused by wind and sun might kill off the unprotected mosses and leave a bald outcrop. Almost anything might happen – if the habitat were left alone and undisturbed.

But no forest in the taiga grows forever undisturbed – except in theory. The African ecologist who called the Canadian boreal forest a newcomer, also said, wisely, "The term climax-vegetation seems hardly applicable to any aspects of this community." For in fact, fire will overtake every part of the taiga, sooner or later. And if fire doesn't break out, the insects will. Forest fire and insect outbreak seem an integral and inescapable – and perhaps natural and necessary – part of the taiga ecology. The tent caterpillars attack the aspen to the benefit of the young balsam fir that were overshadowed. The spruce budworms attack the balsam fir and white spruce to the benefit of the black spruce, whose tough acid needles repel them. When the budworm outbreak dies down the balsam fir, with its aggressive quick-growing seedlings, is best able to regain ground quickly – unless every seed-producing host tree has been killed off, in which case, the shrubs move in or, if there are alders nearby, alder-suckers. Forest fire has the same differential effect. Much depends on its severity, the species present, the time of year in relation to seed-crop, and the nature of the habitat itself, so the logic is complex. But in general fire favours the species that can sprout or disseminate seed widely afterwards. Thus it benefits the poplar and birch (and the black spruce in its fight against choking ground cover) more than the white spruce and balsam fir, at least initially. For in a way fire benefits the whole forest. *Any* natural disturbance – budworm, beaver dam, browsing deer, storm damage – benefits this boreal forest. It is not yet settled in or at home here, and disturbance gives second chances. It keeps the species shifting ground. It keeps them testing both the environment and each other. The undisturbed forest of theory hangs on in decadence. Disturbance, instead, brings constant struggle and constant renewal, which in its own way is a kind of immortality.

SCOURGES OF THE NORTH

The black fly

The cool, clear and swift-running water (1) of northern streams is the habitat of the high-oxygen-demanding black fly. The larvae which occur in streams attach themselves (2) to stones and reeds by means of a disc-like sucker at the posterior end of the body. The larvae are somewhat club-shaped, swollen at the rear, and move about like a measuring worm, motion being aided by silk spun from their mouths. Strainers at the head (3) gather and sift passing food. The larvae pupate in cone-shaped cases (4) resting on objects in the water. During this period, the pupae do not eat, and can only breathe through pupal brushes, or respiratory filaments which act like gills on a fish. The black fly emerges after pupation (5) with its short legs, broad wings and humpbacked appearance and, though it takes to the air to pester livestock, it is still most frequently encountered near streams where the larvae occur. Only the females are blood-sucking, and their bites have proven to be very harmful. Their favourite clime is in the north temperate, sub-arctic zone.

5

1

Maggots and mites

The rat-tail maggot is the larva of the flower fly and favours life in a stagnant, polluted pond (far left). Because of its long tube, the larva (centre left) can survive in any decaying organic material and still breathe in as much oxygen as it requires, existing just beneath the surface film of the water. The flower fly belongs to a large group of which many species abound all in different habitats. The adult flower fly (left) resembles, and therefore imitates, bees so that other animals avoid it. The flower fly itself does not bite though it is sometimes responsible for intestinal myiasis in man.

Water mites are commonly creatures of murky water and, because of their predatory ways, have been called wolves of the water. Clusters of eggs, glued to plants, stones or twigs (1) are watched over by the female adult. A larva emerges from an egg (2), and soon attaches itself to a host insect (3). After a good meal, the larval mite enters a dormant period, corresponding to the pupal stage, during which drastic anatomical alterations occur (4). A new life form, the non-reproductive nymph emerges from the old crust which is still attached to the host, and swims about for food. The nymph then enters a further resting period during which time the adult skin is being formed. Ultimately, the adult breaks through the nymph skin (5) to take its place in the water (overleaf).

2

4

3

5

PART FOUR / ANIMAL LIFE

15 ARMIES OF THE NORTH

A few years ago, during a discussion on the temperament of the North American taiga and tundra environments – where the mere passage of a hunting party may alter vegetation patterns for a century – a Canadian permafrost expert made one qualification: "In some areas of bare rock and no soil development," he remarked, "we could set off an atomic bomb and the area wouldn't look appreciably different afterward from the way it did before."

He was talking about a major fraction of the Canadian Shield. The tundra elsewhere, and indeed the low tundra of the Shield, close to the treeline, is carpeted with vegetation, carries a protective snow cover in winter, and is actually a complex mosaic of habitats, each with its characteristic association of plants and animals. But the high tundra of the Shield is no more than rock desert. The northern half of Ungava Peninsula falls within this rock desert zone. And right in the middle of it something very like an atomic bomb has in fact fallen. It was a meteorite. Someone has calculated that the impact must have equalled a thousand Hiroshima bombs. It has produced the largest known meteorite crater in the world, the New Quebec Crater, still known as the Chubb Crater. The crater is a thousand feet deep and two miles in diameter, with an encircling collar thrust up three hundred feet above the surrounding gneiss plains. Though there is no detectable inlet or outlet, water has seeped in from somewhere to fill the crater with a lake. Perhaps the slow recoil of the Shield from glaciation has cut it off from earlier sources; in any case the lake is now landlocked.

It is hard to imagine anything bleaker than this twice-sterile landscape. From the vantage point of the crater rim, nothing can be seen from horizon to horizon but knobby rock and boulder scree, mile after mile after mile. The leader of the first scientific overland expedition to the crater in 1950, Dr. V. Ben Meen of the Royal Ontario Museum, called the place "this cold emptiness" and compared it to a deserted planet. In a summer's work there, the expedition members saw only three animals: two Arctic foxes and a lemming. The only vegetation, besides patches of lichen and moss, consisted of a few isolated specimens of Arctic cotton grass, Arctic poppy and dwarf willow growing from cracks in the rock, and one species of heather. Not even the willow grew more than nine inches high. The plankton count in the landlocked crater lake was far below the level judged necessary to support healthy fish life.

Yet there were birds in the area. Though the expedition members reported that bird life seemed scarce, they were able to record a fair variety of species: snow buntings, American pipits, northern horned larks, Lapland longspurs, sandpipers, semi-palmated plovers, golden plovers, herring gulls, Arctic terns, common loons, red-throated loons, duck hawks and a lone eagle. And in the crater lake, mysteriously, there proved to be Arctic char, a northern fish of the trout family.

And linking the birds and fish into community with the impoverished vegetation were the insects. At sundown the male midges danced, swarming like thin rising columns of smoke. Midges look like small weak mosquitoes, though they do not bite; indeed about half of them have no mouths and take no food at all in their brief adult life. But they are food for other forms of life. So are their eggs, which are laid in the water in chains, like link sausage, and are coated in a gelatin that swells as it absorbs water, twisting the imprisoned egg-chains into a spiral coil. The gelatin blobs, each containing several hundred eggs, sway temptingly with each movement of the water.

The larva stage makes food for hunters as well. These are the so-called "blood-worms," which hatch from the eggs, sink to the bottom and develop true oxygen-bearing haemoglobin instead of the thin green or yellow serum that serves most insects in place of blood. So fecund are the midges all over the north that pond bottoms have been found to be three-deep in blood-worms. When the blood-worms have fed on enough waterborne organic materials to have become full grown they go through a pupa stage at the surface of the water, and when the midge is fully developed inside the pupa, it splits the skin along the back and crawls out into the air to dry, ready to swarm and mate and start the cycle again.

The expedition's marine biologist found quite a lot of midges in the stomachs of the char. He also found stone-flies, caddis flies, mosquitoes, black flies, adult moths, beetles, wasps, ants and a muscoic fly, a scavenging relative of the housefly. Insect life had seemed as scant as any other kind, yet here was a whole secret population to knit together a web of life. Most of them were insects that feed on plant substances, either in the water or on land. Even among the scanty lichens and in the landlocked lake each had found some niche that could support it. Others, like the wasps and beetles, were meat eaters who had moved in to live on the vegetarians. And both kinds, insect prey and insect predator, were in turn feeding the fish. They were bringing the birds as well: the insect foragers such as the sandpipers and the northern horned larks. Higher in the food chain, the insect-fed fish were bringing the fish-eating birds: loons and herring gulls, and the eagle. And the smaller birds brought their own predators the duck hawks, also called peregrine falcons. All the birds would be hosts to biting lice and other parasites, and some might even die of them.

And the windborne plant and animal debris, along with the lime droppings from the birds, would collect here and there in cracks and depressions in the rock, making a thin organic mat in which a willow or some other plant might root. And here, at the other end of the food chain, the expedition members found springtails.

Springtails are agents of decay. They are tiny primitive wingless insects like lice, and they are called springtails because they have their own pogo-sticks: a tail-like piece that latches under the abdomen and that will, when released, throw the insect hundreds of times its own length. They are also called snow fleas: in winter so many will work their way up through the snow to the surface that they will tinge it reddish or blackish according to their own colour. They live in the damp and dark, feeding on dead vegetation and breaking it down mechanically and chemically into reusable forms. Elsewhere along with mites, which are relatives of the spider, they are the most abundant insects in soil, occurring by the hundreds and thousands per acre. Even here where there was no true soil, springtails had found the organic fillings in the rocks and lichen mats and established themselves.

In many ways insects are the most interesting and suggestive index there is to the whole quality of Shield life. In the mixed forest of the more or less temperate southern fringes of the Shield, there are some twenty thousand species. At the treeline there are about ten thousand species. Just beyond the treeline the number takes a sharp drop to something like a thousand species. In the rock desert of the far tundra there are probably no more than three hundred. (In the high Arctic there may be only twenty-four.) Which types, which families, which orders have dropped out and which have succeeded?

On the southern fringes of the Shield, as in the tropical cradle of all life, the four major orders of insects are still almost equally well represented. The so-called Big Four are those that managed to develop complete metamorphosis: the useful multi-stage life cycle. They are the *Coleoptera*, or beetles; the *Lepidoptera*, or moths and butterflies; the *Hymenoptera*, or wasps and bees, and the *Diptera*, or two-winged flies. Among them, the four orders include the overwhelming majority of insect species now living— and they account for most of the twenty thousand kinds in the Great Lakes-St. Lawrence forest. Most of the families within the orders are well represented too. This is still a comparatively complex environment, with all sorts of ways of making a living.

Life in the boreal forest is tougher, though: the growing season is shorter, the winters are more severe and, above all, the vegetation is simpler. The plant variety is only a third as rich as, say, that of the Laurentian Highlands. And the conspicuous plants are the trees. Along with the lakes and rivers, trees – and the duff on the forest floor – furnish the obvious habitats. So here, though the four orders are still in balance, the families and species have been weeded out to favour the aquatic insects, and those that depend one way or another on trees.

The forest litter is still full of springtails and spider mites, but the earthworms have dropped out: earthworms for some reason don't like the acid soil that evergreens foster. Grasshoppers are noticeably scarce, and the ants here are wood-ants.

The omnipresent beetle seems to be the wood-boring longicorn. The longicorns are a family of beetles, named for their long antennae, whose larvae specialize in eating wood. These beetle larvae reach such numbers in the forest that the sound of their boring through solid wood is quite unmistakable whenever one stops to listen.

In the same way, the significant wasp representative is also a wood specialist: the sawfly. Sawflies are the little reddish, yellow, black or blue wasps that hang motionless wherever a shaft of light strikes through the forest canopy.

They are called sawflies because the ovipositors of the female wasps come equipped with saw-toothed blades with which they make incisions for their eggs in plant tissue. When the larvae

hatch they are as easily recognized as the adults. They are generally greenish, have large bulbous heads and a pair of legs on every segment of the body, and they lie in a curled position like a watch-spring when they are disturbed. If they are picked up they immediately curl and squirt a light yellow liquid, usually foul-smelling, from pores on the sides of the body. In this stage they are greedy feeders on tree foliage, and whole stands of tamarack and pine have been defoliated and destroyed in sawfly outbreaks.

It is true of the sawfly. It is true of the forest tent-caterpillar, which breaks out recurrently wherever there are aspen stands. And it is above all true of the *Lepidoptera* order's most conspicuous boreal forest member, the spruce budworm.

The mechanism of outbreak is ill-understood. The build-up seems to happen when there have been several dry sunny seasons in a row. Balsam fir or white spruce, rather than black spruce, are the victims, for they bud earlier in the spring – just about the time the budworm larvae are emerging from hibernation.

Perhaps the series of dry seasons synchronises the moment precisely. Certainly if the larvae emerge either earlier or later than the peak flowering moment they take longer to mature and are markedly less fertile as adults. On the other hand an inordinately dry and sunny summer is known to force flower production in the fir, breaking its normal two-year flowering cycle. Perhaps the repetition of such summer sends the trees into a frenzy of fertility which is matched by the budworm: in only six generations the spruce budworm can increase ten thousand times.

In any case, sporadically throughout the boreal forest the budworms reach epidemic proportions. Some August, little dun-coloured moths will suddenly be as thick as snowflakes, whirling in grey clouds round the tree tops. These are the adults. The larvae hatch the same season, over-winter on the trees, and emerge in the spring ready to feed. They are bristly, inch-long, olive-brown caterpillars with shiny black heads, yellowish lateral stripes, and a voracious appetite. And the bigger they grow the more they eat. There was a budworm outbreak in 1945 in the Black Sturgeon Lake area north of Thunder Bay. Observers calculated that the population had built up from the normal

The cedar waxwing, here attempting to keep the young fed, finds the bulk of its food in the form of fruits but it also feeds on insects.

thousand larvae per acre to somewhere around 376,000 per acre, and one of them wrote, "Their numbers were appalling. The dropping of excreta from the larvae to the herbs and ground sounded like the patter of rain, and all the plant growth and the exposed ground surface beneath the trees were sprinkled thickly with this excreted material." The outbreak wore itself out only with the large scale death of the host trees.

After a budworm outbreak, the populations of the bark-and wood-boring beetle larvae build up to a peak, infesting the dead trees. And where insect populations are so swollen, there will be the predators: the spiders. Except at the peak of a budworm outbreak, spiders outnumber any species of true insect on the balsam fir. About 75,000 spiders per acre have been counted in the boreal forest.

It has been said that the boreal forest insects are the typical insects of Canada. If so, it is worth noting that the similar fir budworm that is found in the forests of northern Europe remains quietly endemic, with no such periodic explosions as in Canada.

And it is worth noting as well, that though the black fly is almost worldwide in distribution, it reaches its greatest numbers here in the boreal forest of the Shield. Black flies have a specific need for cool, shallow, rapidly moving water. The adult lays her eggs on or in the water and the other three stages, egg, larvae and pupa, are not only aquatic but need a quick turnover of water to provide both oxygen and a continuous food supply. The glaciated Shield, with its juvenile drainage, offers ideal conditions, so that of all the *Diptera* it is the black fly family that predominates here. (The black fly has had a profound effect on the life of the Shield, for it has inhibited both settlement and development. It breeds and bites in the brief, crucial summer working season. A Recollet Brother who travelled up the Ottawa River in 1623-24 wrote afterwards, "I confess that this is the worst martyrdom I suffered in this country.")

Two species attack humans in particular. Other species attack any mammal. Some prey specifically on birds: a pond in Ungava suffered 100 per cent mortality of the ducks from black flies. Black flies have been seen feeding on deer ears, and the nose of a turtle. A black fly has been found with ant juice in its belly. One species, attracted to a specific chemical in the preening gland, bites only loons.

There are sixty Canadian species, and they infest the Shield in numbers that stagger the imagination. A researcher estimated at sixteen million the number of black fly eggs on a single fifteen-foot rock outcrop in a Quebec waterfall. Most species go through two or more generations in a season.

The small, glistening, yellow eggs are laid in compact masses of two to five hundred or so on stream-edge vegetation, stones, submerged deadheads or anywhere else where they will be continually wetted. In one of the species that attacks humans, the eggs hatch and spend the winter in the larva stage, ready to emerge as the early-spring plague of black flies. In the second species, the eggs over-winter without hatching, thus providing a second wave of adults later in the season. The black fly season starts as early as the end of April, reaches a peak in June and July, and can persist well into October; the season shortens progressively towards the north.

The larvae hatch in such numbers that underwater objects often seem carpeted in them. They are ugly little worms with sucker-like legs with which they anchor themselves to submerged surfaces, spinning silken threads to act as additional lifelines against the current. They breathe through the skin and feed on plankton which is swept into the mouth by brushes attached to the head. In the pupa stage they are protected by tiny open-ended cocoons attached at the upstream end. During the pupal state they go on absorbing oxygen from the water, and when they are ready to emerge as adults they pop to the surface inside a bubble of air. In the instant the bubble breaks, these new adults must take to the air, for otherwise they would get their wings wet and drown.

The male adult is a tiny humpbacked iridescent two-winged fly, with huge eyes that have a quite visible reddish tinge. The female has smaller eyes, and is lighter in colour. Both feed on nectar as a source of energy for flight. But the female needs protein – a so-called blood meal – to mature her eggs.

Only the female bites. She doesn't bite as the mosquito does, by inserting a tube and sipping, but by cutting a hole with her saw-edged mouthparts and lapping the blood. She may take up to eight minutes to feed at the open wound.

She doesn't take as much blood as a female mosquito does; she bites only to provide nourishment to complete the egg development and only when the humidity is between seventy and ninety and the wind is light; and, though she is out at dusk and dawn, she retires at night to the protection of the shrubbery and branches. But the bites of the female black flies have a considerable effect. The bites generally swell and itch, and in some people they develop into weeping pustules that last as long as a month. In a few people the sensitivity goes further: there is nausea and fever, the neck gets stiff and the lymph nodes swell. And there are documented cases of death resulting from massive attacks by black flies. The psychological allergy can be almost as striking. Dr. Bryan Hocking of the University of Alberta has reported that under intensive attack, many men become "ineffective" from mental stress: "The rapidity with which a susceptible person can become worked up into an emotional state bordering on dementia . . . has to be seen to be believed." Cattle have died within fifteen minutes of a black fly attack, in a state suspiciously resembling shock. Though black flies have been widely studied, no one seems to know yet what the female does, or injects, that produces these effects.

But nothing is more extraordinary about the black fly family than what happens to it beyond the boreal forest, as it gets towards Baffin Island and the northern limit of its range. In the typical boreal forest species, the young female hatches, flies immediately, mates in flight at one of the black fly swarming sites, flies in search of her blood meal and then settles down to digest it and mature her eggs. As soon as the eggs are laid she flies in search of another blood meal and matures another clutch. This may happen several times in a season. In eight of the nine Arctic species the female has lost her cutting mouthparts and doesn't bite at all. She develops her eggs from nutrients stored up while she was still in the larval stage. And instead of seeking out a mating swarm, she crawls around on the ground in the neighbourhood of her emergence site, depending on a chance encounter with a male.

These are dramatic modifications for an insect to evolve in its life-cycle, and they are a telling illustration of the qualitative increase in the hardships of life beyond the treeline. In a regime of bitter winds and bad climate, the black fly has developed a way to avoid the most dangerous and chancy activity in its life. By foregoing the normal mating procedure and finding a sub-

A male midge resembles a giant mosquito, though it does not bite. They exist for three days as adults only for the purpose of mating.

stitute for the blood meal, the black fly has eliminated the need for any flight at all. Two of the most northerly species have gone even further: they have eliminated the male. The female simply lays unfertilized eggs which produce more females. This is, the experts have concluded, the response of an organism at the absolute limits of its physiological tolerance.

The treeline is the dividing line. Beyond it, both habitat and climate worsen steadily. Even with extended days in summer, the heat-budget from a sun low on the horizon is so small that butterflies have to bask in its direct rays for a while to get enough radiant energy for flight. And mosquito larvae in a partly shaded tundra pool have been seen to cluster and follow the sun clockwise round the pool in the course of the day.

Most northern insects have a form of anti-freeze in the blood which allows them to tolerate very low temperatures, and even freezing. And most of them have adapted to the long harsh winters and brief summers by what is called "opportunism" – the prolonging of the larval stage over one, or even two or more seasons, so that it can store enough nutrients to fuel the brief, carefully timed moment of mating and reproduction. But on the tundra the wind is strong and has an unbroken sweep, so that many insects tend to crawl rather than fly: the bumble bee, the only bee that ranges this far north, even pollinates flowers in this way. And of course the available habitats are more and more restricted.

So at the treeline the number of insect species drops sharply to about a thousand, and the number keeps dwindling from there on northward. Whole families have dropped out. Suddenly there seem to be no dragonflies, or grasshoppers or ants. There are only a few kinds of butterflies, and only the one kind of bee. In fact the whole familiar balance of insect life has been destroyed, for two whole orders, the *Lepidoptera* and the *Coleoptera*, have virtually disappeared.

In contrast the two-winged flies, the *Diptera*, seem almost to have taken over. The warble flies belong to the *Diptera* order. These are the small flies whose larvae are parasites on the caribou. The eggs are laid on the fine woolly down of the undercoat, and when they hatch the larvae penetrate the skin and travel through the body until they come to rest just under the skin on either side of the backbone, where they bore air holes through the skin. The following year the larvae leave the host through these air holes, drop to the ground and pupate. Some 1,000 larvae have been recorded from the back of a single animal.

The caribou, and other deer as well are attacked by another parasitic member of the *Diptera* order, the bot fly. The female bot fly hovers in front of the animal's nose and keeps darting into a nostril to deposit drops of fluid each containing one or more larvae. The bot flies are not so numerous as the warble flies, but they are maddening to the animal, and the irritation of the larvae induces sneezing and catarrh. One reindeer was found playing host to as many as 130 bot fly grubs.

But the truly conspicuous *Diptera* representatives in the tundra, besides the black fly, are the midges and the mosquitoes. The male midges sometimes swarm so thickly that it looks like smoke from a peat fire out of control – ominous enough that even an old northern hand has been known to go and investigate. And the mosquitoes reach their greatest pest level here. An estimate of five million per acre around Hudson Bay is considered conservative.

It is important to notice that the mosquitoes and midges, like the black fly, are aquatic insects. Except for mating and reproduction, they spend their lives in the water, and water is a protected environment. In the worst sub-zero weather, water, under its thick layer of ice, never gets colder than about 39°F.

It is equally important to notice that the warm body of a host animal is also a protected environment. The *Diptera* are successful north of the treeline because they have produced so many species that are either parasitic or aquatic. In the same way, the selected species from the other orders that have managed to succeed in the tundra and Arctic are mainly aquatic, like the stone-flies and caddis flies, or they are parasitic. The noticeable member of the wasp family is not the sawfly, as in the boreal forest, but the ichneumon wasp, whose larvae cling to their hosts and feed through puncture wounds. The biting lice, too, though they belong to a minor order, are notably successful in the north.

There is one other protected environment, in this harsh land, and that is the soil. Like the water, it too buffers the ambient temperatures. And so another minor order, the *Collembola*, is more successful in the north than hundreds of thousands of species belonging to the Big Four. The *Collembola* are the spring-tails. They have been found as far north as Ellesmere Island.

16 SONGSTERS OF THE WOODS

To many people, all wilderness is in the night cry of a loon. They would argue for this reason, and because it is the most ancient surviving bird species, (its record is at least sixty million years long), and because it is a creature of the remote lakes, that it is the bird synonymous with the Canadian Shield.

Others would argue that the gray jay – the impudent and intelligent whisky-jack of woods and campsites – is the more indigenous bird. Unlike the loon, it winters as well as summers in the forests of the Shield and it is, after all, known as the Canada jay.

Still others would make claims for the familiar scavenging raven of the north, or for the three-toed woodpeckers, whose home is the boreal forest. Those who knew the tundra best might think of the thronging godwits and dunlins and sandpipers of the flats. Anyone who had been near the 1800-foot pinnacle of Cap Tourmente, on the Quebec North Shore, in September or October when fifty thousand snow geese made their annual stopover from their high Arctic breeding grounds, would be forgiven for calling this the Shield's most unforgettable bird.

But the birds that make the real difference to the Shield are the wood warblers.

In the spruce forests of the Baltic Shield there are commonly fewer than a hundred pairs of breeding birds per hundred acres – about one pair per acre and a quarter. Most of them would be recognizable to a Canadian birdwatcher: thrushes sing from the shadows; titmice and kinglets hang upside down from the twig tips and woodpeckers test the dead branches just as they do in Shield woodlands. But in Shield woodlands more than two hundred pairs of birds per hundred acres are to be found – more than twice as many. The difference is the warblers. Warblers make up more than half the summer breeding population of the boreal forest. One bumper season, in the Lake Nipigon region, more than six pairs per acre were counted. This is six times the Baltic average. Four of the six pairs were warblers.

Wood warblers are entirely a New World group. They seem to have evolved in the mid-Pleistocene period and they belong to that elite order of the bird world, the passerines, or songbirds. The passerines are relatively modern birds and because of their numbers, the number of species, and their wide distribution, they are counted – along with the insects and the rodents – as the great evolutionary successes of the animal kingdom.

Warblers are tiny hyperactive birds, usually no more than five inches long. They have small needle-point bills and they eat almost nothing but insects. So many of them are so vivid, with such paint-bright patchwork markings, that the Latin Americans call them mariposas – "butterflies." It has been suggested that a billion would be too conservative an estimate of their numbers. Their headquarters are in the mountainous regions of Central and South America and about half of the 116 or so species spend their whole lives in the tropics.

The rest may spend two-thirds of their year in the tropics, but they migrate to breed. Indeed some warblers are among the epic migrants of the world. For example, given its breeding and wintering ranges, the minimum journey the blackpoll warbler makes cannot be less than 3,500 miles one way. Those that nest in Alaska and winter in Brazil make journeys of seven thousand miles. Since it's probable that they don't travel in a perfectly straight line, some blackpolls may fly a 20,000 mile round-trip in a year.

And the routes some warblers take make it likely that numbers of them fly non-stop for sixty to seventy hours or more. Warblers in fall have been tracked by radar until they were out of range, striking out southeasterly over the open ocean from the coast of Massachusetts. Their probable destinations in the Antilles or Venezuela were on that heading; they were flying at a steady twenty-five to thirty miles an hour; and sixty or seventy hours of such flying would bring them to their goal.

No one really knows how migrating birds find their way, except that it seems to be by some form of celestial navigation. No one really knows why certain species of birds took to the migration habit at all: food supply in the breeding season seems an obvious answer, and yet it begs several questions. (One of them is how the 116 warbler species decided which half could stay around headquarters and which half had to leave.)

Indeed no one really knows whether the warblers actually originated in the tropics or whether, instead, the migrating members are remnants of an old tribe that evolved in a warmer, pre-

Finding their way

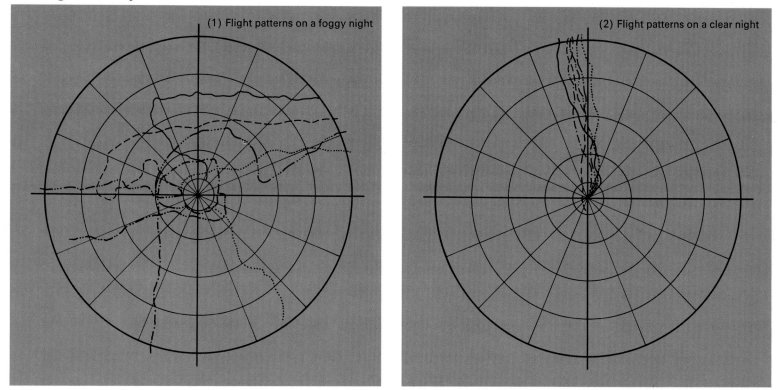

(1) Flight patterns on a foggy night

(2) Flight patterns on a clear night

Birds appear to navigate at night with the aid of the stars. Two sets of mallards with small flashlights attached to their feet for observation purposes were released on foggy and clear nights respectively. While the mallards in the foggy weather set off in all directions, unable to see the stars (1), those in clear conditions immediately started off, and continued in, the right direction, due north (2).

glacial North America toward which they home when it's time to breed. But in any case, forty-two species of warblers make the annual trip to Canada. Of these, some eighteen are important in the boreal forest of the Shield.

They come, these particular ones, from the coffee plantations of Central America, from the West Indies, from Mexico and Panama, from the Andean valleys and Guyanan forests, from as far away as Venezuela and Peru. Only one hasn't so far to go: the stubborn and hardy little myrtle warbler which can live on winter berries and fruits even when there are no insects. The myrtle warbler, a streaky little bird with a white throat and a clear yellow rump, has its main wintering range no farther south than the coast of the Carolinas, and has even been known to overwinter in Toronto.

But even as early as February, after a winter of going about

their separate tropical businesses, the rest have begun to acquire the bright crisp courting plumage and are starting to become gregarious again, to congregate in flocks. For the warblers, as any birdwatcher knows, come north in waves.

They begin to leave the south in late March in mixed bands of several species. They fly by night and forage by day, and at first the only sound they utter is a call-note to each other that keeps them together during their night flight. About two-thirds of the way through the trip, though, they begin practising the songs that are their burglar alarms on the breeding grounds: the songs that proclaim each pair's territory by warning off trespassers. Though they belong to the order of song-birds, and are themselves called warblers, most warblers have songs of approximately the same musicality as frogs or crickets. All sorts of people have tried either descriptive or phonetic notation as an aid to identification. The parula warbler, for example, has been assigned "a sizzling gurgle" which is rendered as "zzzzzzzzzzzzz-zip" (1¾ seconds) followed by "bz-bz-bz-bz-bz-zzzzzzzzzz-up" (1½ seconds). The most apt comment still seems that of an early authority, Frank Chapman, who wrote, "One's best attempts at description after a time are often meaningless to oneself." But the sound of a warbler wave, to anyone who has heard one, is unmistakable: the woods and thickets and underbrush are full of little teasing lisps and buzzes.

Probably tens of thousands of warblers die during every migration. They are buffeted by storms, they are easily hypnotised by beacons, against which they dash themselves, and they sometimes outrace the advance of spring. Louise Lawrence, a naturalist who kept records for two decades in the Mattawa River country of Ontario, has written an account of one disaster that overtook a spring migration wave in 1956.

It was brought on by a late, brutally cold spring, broken by a sudden three-day heatwave that sent the temperature to 83 degrees, thus triggering a visible swelling of buds and colouring of branches, followed by an overnight snowstorm and ten-day freeze. At first the migrants held back farther south, each day's new arrivals adding to the pressure of numbers that was building up. The three-day thaw sent them all racing ahead, trying to mend their schedules. The cold snap caught them in the night and brought them down. Mrs. Lawrence describes the scene on the first morning: "They came on this day, not through the trees, but crawling, hopping stiffly from straw to dead leaf, covering the ground with their bodies . . . ovenbirds (a kind of warbler) walked all over the forest floor and in places sheltered from the snow turned over the dead leaves, one by one, looking for a snail, a mite, whatever edible thing the leaf might cover. Nashville warblers, bright yellow dots in the snow, fed ravenously upon the yellow stamens of the pussy-willows . . . . All through the day the birds moved slowly and laboriously northward across the Pimisi Bay region in the teeth of the piercing wind, hugging the ground . . . ." Dead birds by the score were picked up all through the area.

Straggling groups continued to come during the whole ten days, always travelling close to the ground in a fruitless search for the insects that should have been hatching by now. With no way to take inventory in the wilderness, Mrs. Lawrence does not venture to estimate the death toll by starvation and exposure of the ten freezing days. But she does report a conspicuous decline in numbers of song-birds, particularly the warblers, the following year. If it had been a lesser disaster, the population losses should have been made up by then.

It is the time of the insect hatch on the chosen breeding ground, rather than the temperature, that regulates the northward movement of the warblers. And nothing better suggests the extravagant annual explosion of life in the boreal forest than this contingent invasion by millions of warblers.

The closer they get to their destination, the faster they travel, so that the blackpolls who started by loitering through the deep south at thirty-five miles per day finish their trip at an average of two hundred miles per day. They have the farthest to go.

The others drop out individual by individual and species by species, as they find their preferred conditions. For, like all living things, each warbler species has a niche. A niche has been defined as an organism's specialty: its unique way of making a living. Thus, for example, small woodpeckers forage from bottom to top of a tree, removing grubs from those cracks most accessible from underneath; while nuthatches work downward feeding from the cracks more accessible from above. Though they may use the same tree, each has his niche. A niche has been more broadly defined, though, as the combination of an organism's food and enemies: as his role in the whole ecological system.

At least one of the Shield warblers has an almost unbelievably specialized niche. Kirtland's warbler, a big, gentle warbler that is grey above and yellow below, nests only in a sixty mile-wide belt in north-central Michigan. In this belt, it nests only in pure groves of baby jackpines, bushing low enough to conceal its nest on the ground. The jackpines must be no less than three and no more than about a dozen feet high. It is so fastidious in its choice that some Michigan State forest lands have been designated as preserves for Kirtland's warbler, to be cut or burnt over regularly to provide the right habitat.

So the Kirtland's warblers will already have dropped out of the warbler migration in Michigan. Another warbler with a recherché taste in nesting sites is the pretty and friendly little parula warbler, whose more descriptive name used to be blue yellow-backed warbler. The northern parula insists on making its nest of *Usnea*, the old man's beard lichen, so it disappears to the areas where *Usnea* grows thickest: which in Canada means the dankest parts of the Great Lakes – St. Lawrence forest.

Some part of this forest, with its complexity and variety of habitats, seems to be the goal for some of almost every warbler species that comes into the country. The American redstarts, with their red-and-black flamenco colouring and their habit of fanning the tail to show it off, haunt the woodlots. Wherever there are good big clearings, even in areas built up with cottages, the yellows will settle. They don't mind humans. The yellows have faint red pinstripes down their fronts, but the rest of their bodies are so purely the colour of egg-yolk that they are often mistaken for escaped pet canaries.

Scuffing through the leaves on the forest floor is the little brown oven bird, with its big eyes, striped breast and dull orange crown. There are three warblers that look like small thrushes and walk on the ground and the oven-bird is one of them. Up above, working over the bark of the hardwoods for insects, just like a tree creeper, is the black-and-white warbler, patterned like a black-and-white woodcut. And foraging in the leafy depths of the mature hardwood forest is the black-throated blue, with its quaint air of formality.

But the mature deciduous forest is not a preferred location: with its high closed canopy and its empty shady aisles, it doesn't support much insect life. The evergreen stands are better: they are upside-down trees, open to light and widening layers of growth from spire to bushy lower branches. In the sun they buzz with insects.

The warblers divide up the riches, each kind appropriating its own stratum. The Canada stays close to the ground, snapping at insects in the little open glades between the lowest boughs. The Canada is a fat little fop with a pearl-grey back, a clear yellow breast and a rayed necklace of black stripes bold against the yellow. The blackburnian, all hot orange throat and sooty streaks, feeds higher. The black-throated green's territory is usually out of sight among the topmost branches. He is not exactly green: his back is olive-yellow, his cheeks are clear yellow and his front is white; but he has a black throat as advertised. Still, he is more often heard than seen: a dreamy summer buzz from the treetops.

In contrast the Cape May warbler looks bold and takes a bold open perch. He is tiger-striped in black and yellow, with russet earmuffs, and he lights to sing wherever an isolated spruce spire stands above the rest. But his song is weak, and so high-pitched that it is easily missed.

The glowing little blackburnians, and olive black-throated greens reach their highest numbers right here in hemlocks and pines of the Great Lakes – St. Lawrence forest. But most of the tiger-striped Cape Mays go on into the boreal forest.

Warblers, arriving by the million in spring, help to control the insect population of the boreal forest. All summer these tiny insectivores hunt almost any type of insect as hard as they can, in order to keep the young well supplied with food, and to store up fat for the long flight south.

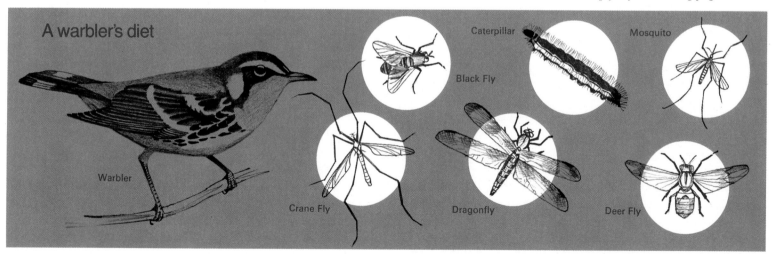

A warbler's diet

Warbler · Black Fly · Caterpillar · Mosquito · Crane Fly · Dragonfly · Deer Fly

So do the bulk of the warblers. For in a belt just south of latitude fifty from Lake Nipigon east to the interior of the Gaspé Peninsula the northern warblers reach their greatest abundance. Here, too, each species spreads out to find its niche. The troops of Cape Mays find their lofty spruce-spire singing perches in the densest part of the mature forest. Avoiding the tops, and feeding somewhat below them are the bay-breasted warblers, large russet, cream and grey warblers with black robber masks. The bay-breasted warblers are considered rare birds elsewhere, but here in the heart of boreal forest they are the dominant birds. Where the forest is more open and dappled with light the Tennessees are dominant, though scarcely conspicuous: they are drab little birds with soft olive colouring and only a faint white eyeline to distinguish them.

The magnolias prefer still more ragged woodland, with sturdy new conifer seedlings pushing up to make a dense second-growth. The magnolias are vivid little scraps that look as if they had been marked with poster-paint: all black streaks and white splotches on bright yellow and clear grey. The low feeding grey-hooded mourning warblers forage in burnt or cut-over areas.

All through this area of warbler concentration, wherever there are spruce bogs, there are the similar Connecticut warblers and Nashville warblers – yellow-breasted, both helmeted in grey – and the palm warblers, with their stripes, chestnut caps and constant, nervous tail-wagging.

Though this eastern belt of boreal forest is warbler country, these same species in these same niches can be found all across the Shield. The only difference is that in the spruce bogs of the western part, from Manitoba to Alberta, the demure mouse-like little orange-crowned warbler (even the orange crown is concealed most of the time) is more common than the tail-flicking palm warbler.

But, east or west, it is the distance champion blackpoll that pushes, faster and faster, on and beyond all the rest: on into the tundra; off to the northwest towards the Yukon and Alaska, northeast to the high Labrador coast.

Once he gets there, like all the warblers that dropped out behind him, he sets up a defended area: a territory. Warblers are monogamous. The male birds settle the territories among themselves, and only the successful ones can win a mate. (The leftovers become a sort of standby replacement pool.) For whatever habitat is fancied, each pair of warblers must have room, a proper spot for a nest, nesting material and the correct singing perch, in order to breed successfully. And they must have food.

As in most small birds, digestion in warblers is continuous and their stomachs must be filled many times each day. They are little dynamos when they feed. The tree creeping, bark probing black-and-white has been seen to take twenty-eight browntail caterpillars in ten minutes, and probably took more than that. The canary-like yellow has been seen to eat thirty-three canker worms in a little over six minutes. The tail-twitching palm warbler of the spruce bogs has been observed feeding at the rate of an insect per second. Warblers are sometimes so packed with food that when one is dissected the contents of the stomach will expand to twice or even three times the size of the stomach itself.

And when the four or five eggs are hatched, the activity is redoubled: each young bird requires fully half its own weight of insects each day. But it doesn't last long. In less than two weeks the babies are out of the nest, and soon the adults have begun fraternizing with each other again, and even with other insect-hunting species.

For part of each day an assortment of warblers will join roving bands of chickadees, kinglets, nuthatches, creepers and woodpeckers on what seems to be a regular food-foraging beat. (It takes the same daily path, often an ellipse or a figure eight.) As many as eleven different species have been counted in such mixed bands, and it has been suggested that their function is to take census of the area's insect-eating population in relation to the available food, so that density adjustments can be made if needed. In this view, population is regulated at a group level, both within species and between species, so that it doesn't overshoot the carrying capacity of the habitat. The adjustments are made in a whole series of ways including variations in the size of the individual territories in order to regulate the number of breeding pairs, and variations in the number of eggs laid, eggs hatched and nestlings properly nursed to maturity.

In any event, the warblers are still feeding as hard as they can. For the great migration south is coming and they fuel their migration flights with stored fat. Even partway through migration, warblers have been found to have thirty per cent of their body weight in fat.

The odd thing is that they leave while the summer bloom is

still on the boreal forest. No one knows exactly what rhythm in their natures sends them off again. But as early as mid-August bands of warblers have begun to drift south, and by September the fall migration is on in earnest. The myrtle warbler is among the last to go. His yellow rump is still a cheerful and identifying flash of colour as late as mid-October, even in his fall camouflage. For the warblers, in fall, trade their op art plumage for the incognito of such similar olive-drab uniforms that Roger Tory Peterson, author of the standard field guide, lumps most of them together as "confusing fall warblers." But at last all the little teasing lisps and buzzes among the branches have faded to the south. The forest has emptied. The warblers have gone.

No one really knows how big the annual invasion may be. But at the very least, given the figure of one pair per acre, there must be on an average something like 700 million in the boreal forest alone. There have been some interesting and suggestive discoveries about variations in the warbler population on these northern breeding-grounds. At least some of the species have been found to fluctuate violently: the myrtle warbler, for example, and the bay-breasted and the black-throated green. The population levels in these three species have shown peaks and ebbs on so regular a cycle – every two or three years – that they cannot be explained by chance. And then there are great build-ups: in some years, in certain areas, the warbler population will triple or even quadruple, so that there are as many as four pairs nesting in one acre.

The links in these particular cases have been clear: they are the weather, the spruce and balsam fir, and the spruce budworm that feed on them. These links form a complex and imperfectly understood chain, but it goes something like this: both balsam fir and white spruce have flowering rhythms that can be strikingly affected by the summer weather of the preceding year. Even in normal times, the spruce budworm population reflects the fertility of the conifers; and those warblers that prefer *Lepidoptera* to other insects, and that normally feed in the spruce-fir forest, will in turn echo this waxing and waning in the numbers of their prey. But from time to time, perhaps in response to some weather-triggered explosion of conifer bloom, there will be an explosion in the spruce budworm population. The warbler population was studied at the time of one such outbreak, in 1945, in the area ninety miles north of Thunder Bay. At the height of the outbreak the warblers were crowding each other into territories that were no more than a quarter of an acre, and the competition among them was described as "spectacular." There were twelve species of warbler in the hundred-acre tract where the research was carried out, and among them the population of Cape May warblers had risen to 28 pairs; there were 59 pairs of Tennessee warblers, and 92 pairs of bay-breasted warblers – ten times the normal number. Perhaps these three liked budworms better, and were readier, as species, to take advantage of the feast that the abundance of budworms provided.

But it is worth noting that, though the population of insect-eating birds more than doubled (even the red-eyed vireo, which usually avoids conifers, developed a new method of feeding and moved in to feast on the budworm larvae) it was estimated that they destroyed less than five per cent of the budworms. Rather than the birds controlling the pest, the pest was controlling the number of birds.

There was no follow-up study of the crash that presumably occurred when the budworms had killed off that area of the forest. But there is information from other studies to indicate how complex the inter-relationships in the boreal forest can be. During the outbreak, when the Tennessee, bay-breasted, and Cape May warblers were prospering, the magnolias and blackburnians were virtually crowded out. When the three that dominated the budworm outbreak subsided, it is presumed that the magnolias and blackburnians would benefit. If the warbler population had in some way been destroyed, it is presumed that it would almost instantly have been replaced from outside by what appears to be a floating pool of replacements for such circumstances. If the spruce budworms had been killed off, spider mites would have come in to replace them.

After the outbreak had run its course and the host trees had been killed, it is assumed that the numbers of bark- and wood-boring beetle larvae would have built up to infest the dead trees. And this in turn would have brought a build-up in the populations of three-toed woodpeckers to feed on them. And if the dead trees then caught fire, in time the mourning warblers would move into the burnt-over area; and then, as the forest began to renew itself, other warblers, specific to the second growth, and so on: each ebb and flow of species, each shift and replacement a response to the needs and events of a complex organic whole.

A beaver swims at dusk to its lakeside colony,
with sticks in tow to supplement its winter diet.

17 ANIMALS IN THE WILDS

Some animals of the Shield, like the moose, seem to be in the process of extending their range. Even as recently as a hundred years ago there were two distinct races of moose: a western race that had come only as far east as Thunder Bay, and an eastern race that had followed the retreat of glaciation northward to occupy an area north of a line from Sault Ste. Marie to about Kingston. At Confederation the two races were still many hundreds of miles apart. But the races have met and mingled, and moose now occur continuously through most of the boreal forest from the Gulf of St. Lawrence through to the far northwest. Other Shield animals, such as the lynx and the caribou seem to be both retreating northward and declining in numbers. The reasons for success or failure of animal life in a given environment are always complex – and when the environment itself is as unstable as the Shield seems to be, the distribution and abundance of its animal life has to be thought of as still in flux.

Still, some general observations can be made. The first is that the Shield edge itself imposes no barrier on mammal life: of some fifty-nine species that reach the southern perimeter of the Shield, fifty-four species go on to it and range at least through its southern parts. The largest group of Shield mammals (about a third of the species) are rodents: assorted mice, voles, lemmings and squirrels as well as the woodchuck, the beaver, the muskrat and the porcupine. The carnivores are the second largest group and are almost equally diversified: besides the familiar small fur-bearing animals such as the marten, weasel and fisher, they include the black bear, the lynx, the wolverine, the timber wolf and the Arctic wolf, the red fox and the Arctic fox. There are three ruminants: the moose, the white-tailed deer and the caribou. There are two kinds of bat. Then there is a small but busy and widespread group of shrews and moles. And there are two rabbits: the Arctic hare and, crucial to the boreal forest, the varying or snowshoe hare.

The second observation is that life gets progressively more exacting from south to north: of the species that occur in the southern parts of the Shield, fewer than half range as far as the treeline. Of the twenty-five that reach the treeline, only fourteen venture beyond it, onto the tundra. Of these fourteen only four – the Arctic hare, the Arctic fox, the northern lemming mouse and the Ungava varying lemming – are truly and exclusively tundra species. If the Shield edge is not a biological barrier, the treeline is. This same impoverishment of species towards the poles is, of course, true for all forms of life including the insects, the fish, and the amphibians and reptiles. At the treeline in Ungava there are no reptiles and only two amphibians.

There is a third observation to be made. Winter is the deciding factor. The typical Shield residents have all made special, and in some cases striking, adjustments to the fact of winter. Winter means food shortage. Winter means snow. And winter means extremes of cold. The species that successfully repopulated the Shield after glaciation had to be masters of these conditions. The opossum, which is now trying to extend its range north onto the margins of the Shield in Ontario, is repeatedly found with severe frostbite on ears and tail.

There are some general ways in which species manage to be cold-hardy. For example, increased bulk increases the ratio of heat production to heat loss through the skin. So northern members of a species tend to be larger than their southern relatives. Chipmunks and pygmy shrews near the treeline, for example, are bigger than chipmunks and pygmy shrews farther south. Insulation is another obvious advantage in cold climates, so many of the northern animals have particularly dense and luxuriant coats (and contribute them to the historic Canadian fur trade). As an application of these two principles: boreal animals can be divided into those big enough and sufficiently insulated to follow fairly normal routines through the winter, and those that must make special arrangements. The red squirrel is just on the borderline: he is active when the winter is moderate, but retreats into a burrow if the cold becomes extreme.

Along with a general increase in size of specimens from south to north goes a colour change in the fur: the varying hare, for example, has a richly coloured coat towards the south of its range, but tends to look dull and dingy in the north. It changes its coat to white, in winter, of course. In a similar way, the long-tailed weasel changes to a white coat in winter, but only towards the north of its range. And northern species are apt to have evolved smaller extremities, in order to reduce the risk of frost-bite. Both the Arctic fox and the Arctic hare have shorter ears than their boreal forest cousins, the red fox and the varying hare.

Cold, all by itself, is enough to limit the northward distribution of the amphibians and reptiles. With body temperatures that echo their surroundings, they are profoundly influenced by cold. Most of the reptiles and amphibians in northern Canada spend five to eight months in a state of hibernation. Furthermore, the climate affects their reproduction: the onset of breeding and laying is tied to specific temperatures for each species, and where these temperatures are not reached the species cannot go. Only the wood frog, which can produce viable eggs in water as cold as 36.5°F, reaches the treeline.

Food shortage, more than cold, is the real problem posed by winter. The mammalian body temperature is quite high – nearly 100°F. In the coldest parts of the Shield an animal may have to find enough food to keep its core temperature 150 degrees higher than the temperature of the environment – and at a time when food is at its scarcest. So the moose, whose appetite in summer is for the succulent water-lily shoots in the muskeg, has to move into the forest in winter and dine on the woody bark and twigs of the balsam fir, white birch and trembling aspen. It takes about two square miles of winter forest to supply his needs. The carrying capacity of the same area in summer may be twice as high, but it is this winter requirement, finally, that dictates the density of the moose population. In the same way the white-tailed deer, in winter, turns from lusher pasturage to the bark of trees. And the size of the moose and deer population, in turn, holds the timber wolf population to a maximum density of one for every ten square miles. The timber wolves hunt in packs in the fall and winter: a group approach increases efficiency and is therefore one of their adaptations to food shortage in the hard season.

A number of smaller animals such as the Arctic fox and the big short-tailed shrew, solve the food problem by hoarding against the winter. So does the red squirrel. It has been found that the most elite among the red squirrels defend high-quality sites in the coniferous forest all year round in order to ensure winter provisions. But even the also-rans, which trespass and scrounge around in summer, set up and defend specific winter caches on whatever second-grade sites they can find. One investigator says, "If a squirrel had no territory in the late fall, it would soon starve if it did not find an empty one." But with an adequate food supply the squirrel can stay active all winter; only if the temperature falls to –25°F or –30°F will he tunnel underground for short periods. The beaver, of course, is also a winter hoarder. He cuts between two and three hundred trees a year, hauls them to the pond where he has his lodge, cuts them into segments and uses them either for construction, for the evening meal or for the pantry. But it's to be noted that his appetite in summer when tree-cutting is at a minimum, is mostly for aquatic plants like duckweed, water-lily roots and eelgrass. The beaver too, has to change his diet to get through the winter.

Another group of the smaller animals solves the winter food problem by hibernating. Cold alone doesn't cause hibernation, for some animals will live for months in the cold before sinking into torpor. They seem to enter hibernation from a state of sleep during which the body temperature makes a series of plunges and recoveries – each recovery accompanied by shivering and heart acceleration, each plunge lower than the last – until the temperature of the cave or burrow is reached. If, during the winter, the ambient temperature approaches freezing-point, the animal is able to speed up its metabolism just enough to compensate for it. (Even in hibernation it is fatal for ice to form in a mammal's body tissue. This is why no animal of the high Arctic hibernates: in prolonged, acutely sub-zero weather he cannot prevent slipping over the borderline into freezing.) Waking and rewarming again takes two or three hours and is obviously a tremendous physiological effort: the heart suddenly races a hundred times as fast; the body hair stands erect; breathing is fast and uneven, and the animal shakes as if it had the ague.

Hibernation is generally considered to be an evolutionary dead end, for it involves the deliberate abandonment of warm-bloodedness in order to slow the metabolic processes to an idling speed where no growth takes place and little food is needed. Contrary to the folklore, bears do not qualify as true hibernators, for though they retire to dens in winter and roll up into furry balls, their body temperature does not fall below

Wild beauty in the wilderness

Sharing the sunlight from spring to fall, a variety of wild-flowers brings beauty and sweet fragrance to the rocks and marshes of the Shield. Since insects pollinate the plants, a dazzling variety of flowers appear, to better attract the insects. Thousands of pigments in flowers and fruits provide the beautiful shades and nuances of colour: green from chlorophyll, reds, blues, purples and even white from anthocyanin. The highest forms of plant life are those with enclosed seeds, called angiosperms, or flowering plants. Each species has a preferred location for growing, where conditions meet its needs, and a preferred time of year to burst into bloom. Pictured here are some of those wild-flowers that grow on the Canadian Shield — a proud display, drinking in the morning dew. To moist woodland, where they rise a foot or so high, springtime brings the handsome red trilliums (1) and some of purest white (2) to southern parts of the Shield. There may be as many as three hundred species of violets (3) distributed over the world, and in the Shield their showy blossoms first appear near the streams in spring. A little later, at the time when harebells (4) are just beginning to decorate crevices amongst the rocks with clusters of tiny cup-shapes, the tall columbine (5) nods its graceful head in open woods and meadows. Towards the end of summer, orange hawkweeds (6) brighten dry clearings, and late in the fall, on the verge of frost, fringed gentian (7) flowers in the shady places and around marshes, providing a last dab of bright colour before winter.

1

90°F and they waken easily if prodded. But two of the Shield bats hibernate, as does one carnivore – the skunk – and four rodents – the meadow jumping mouse, the Franklin ground squirrel, the chipmunk and the woodchuck. The woodchuck becomes extremely fat in the fall, and then lives off this fat throughout his hibernation. The chipmunk combines food caching with hibernation and wakens from time to time to feed. Of all the Shield rodents, these four have decided that the metabolic costs of fuelling a normal above-ground winter are too high, and have opted out.

Along with food shortage and the cold, the third fact of winter on the Shield is the snow, particularly in the boreal forest. The snow cover may persist for as much as nine months of the year, a hindrance to both food-getting and locomotion, and the animals must all adapt to the fact. The varying hare, for example, has evolved outsize furry feet that serve it as snowshoes. The moose, on the other hand, has legs as long as stilts to keep its belly clear of the snow surface. These, along with the varying or "hoofed" lemming, form an elite which has made definite physiological adaptations to the snow. But even the moose cannot operate well in more than three feet of snow. When there is more than this, the moose packs the snow in trails or yards.

And the white-tailed deer cannot operate in more than twenty inches. Indeed, depth of snowfall is thought to be defeating the deer's attempts to increase its range northward. For a time, the white-tailed deer was reported as far north as James Bay, but now it has retreated south and is scarcely seen north of North Bay. The deer, too, yard up in winter, collecting in valley bottoms and small groves of trees and packing narrow trails for themselves through herd movement. The concentration of deer in one small area is apt to strip the trees bare up to a browse line, and in years where the snow is deep and persistent, thousands of deer may starve. The smaller, shorter deer will starve first.

The caribou, too, are bullied by the snow. They are driven south by the hard-packed tundra snow that covers their browse, and even in the boreal forest they must congregate where the snow is soft, light and thin enough to be pawed through. Aerial surveys of wintering bands of caribou have shown them shifting about in accordance with snow conditions.

The lynx, too, is affected by the snow. In years when the snow has little bearing strength he gets bogged down. Each leap takes a little longer, and the result, as a study in Alberta has shown, is that his attempts to take snowshoe hare (his main winter food) meet with only nine per cent success as compared to twenty-four per cent when the snow is well-packed.

But for the hibernators, thick snow is a boon. Snow is an effective insulator. The mossy floor of a mature spruce forest under full snow cover seldom drops below 20°F even when air temperatures are fifty or sixty below zero. And so the hibernating mammal can den up here safely. And in this same dark, damp protected environment, vegetation and pupating insects are sheltered. So the smallest mammals of the Shield, the shrews and voles and lemmings, can live and feed safely in mazes of under-snow runways and burrows throughout the winter. As soon as the snow cover reaches a critical depth of six inches they disappear underground. Indeed the period between the onset of sub-freezing weather and the accumulation of the six-inch snow insulation is more dangerous for them than any other part of the winter. Except for this one hazard: a Russian worker has reported that enough carbon dioxide sometimes collects under the snow that the voles have to drive up ventilation shafts. The shafts can be spotted by predators, and the Russian believes that only this circumstance allows some species of owls to survive the subarctic winter.

The borderline between survival and death is very thin, on the Shield. If the snow lasts too long thousands of deer starve to death straining for out-of-reach food. If the temperatures stay too low too long, the hibernating mammals simply freeze to death deep in their burrows. If the muskrat has made his riverbank home too far north he will return from foraging to find the underwater entrance frozen over and he will die of exposure. Small ground-resting birds get trapped and killed by sudden snow. The old and the weak and ill of any species don't live to see the fierce bloom of the following summer: they don't even last till spring.

The life of the Shield has a peculiarly high strung quality, and this is in part given by the contrast between winter and the brief extravagant explosion of summer life. Pollen by the tens of thousands of tons suddenly hangs in visible clouds over the evergreens. The ponds turn green with algae bloom. Billions of insects emerge from cocoons to start feeding. Hundreds of millions of birds appear in the forest. In something like three months whole populations of animals court, mate, give birth and rear their young to self-sufficiency. It is like a bacchanalia.

But there is something beyond this that adds to the impression of touchiness and instability. The summer blooms in some years are excessive, and in other years too meagre to be healthy. The forest tent-caterpillars break out, and then the spruce budworms, and then both die out. The warbler populations build up, some species seem almost to take over, and then they virtually disappear. There is a feeling of flux and disturbed rhythms. The white spruce and balsam fir explode into flower a year too early.

And populations of lemmings and Arctic foxes and snowy owls on the tundra; populations of snowshoe hares and red foxes, lynx, ruffed grouse and prairie grouse in the boreal forest, build up to periodic peaks, and then crash. This is not the measured feast and famine of the seasonal calendar. This is something else.

The phenomenon of dramatic rhythmic fluctuations in some boreal forest populations has been called "the most important problem in North American ecology." The population peaks of lemmings and their predators in the tundra occur about every four years, and this four-year cycle occurs in the tundra of Scandinavia and Siberia as well. But the cycle in the boreal forest, which seems to be timed by the varying hare and which occurs on average every ten years, happens nowhere else in the world. Though it happens throughout the boreal forest, the cycle reaches its most spectacular proportions in the west, from Manitoba to northern Alberta, which is where the varying hare breeds best.

In some ways, the sequence of events is pretty well understood. All it really takes to produce a population explosion is unbridled reproduction. One North American species of field mouse, for example, can breed when it is three weeks old and produce thirteen litters a year.

In the case of the varying hare, the doe can start breeding the spring after she is born. She can bear as many as nine babies in one litter, and produce four, or possibly even five, litters in a season. If every doe including the year's debutantes

met these maximums for several successive seasons, and if the babies had a higher than normal survival rate (it can vary from three per cent survival up to thirty per cent or more), the varying hare population would explode. And so it does. The so-called ten year cycle (it can vary between eight and eleven years) is now being intensively studied in the boreal forest of Alberta. The last varying hare peak occurred in the fall of 1961 and unfortunately the study was not then under way. But, though no accurate figures are available, the population peak was described as "truly incredible." By 1969 the next peak was looming. Populations of up to 7,700 per square mile were being predicted for the fall of 1970. "And if we're out by a year and the peak is not till 1971," said one researcher, "we'll have rabbits coming out of our ears."

Several things will almost certainly happen at the same time. The population of ruffed grouse, which shares the hare's food supply, will build up to a simultaneous peak. The lynx, which prey on both hare and grouse, will build to a peak a year later. If what the fur trade records suggest holds true, some other carnivores such as red foxes, mink and martens will show increases as well. The great horned owls, which feed on both hare and grouse, will also respond. (But predators with more catholic tastes, such as the red-tailed hawk, will not be affected.) And then there'll be a crash.

In some ways, this sequence is also understood. One study that contributed to the understanding was conducted during a varying hare population crash in the forests of Minnesota in the Thirties. The researchers found that hares trapped and nursed in the most favourable possible conditions nevertheless tended to die almost at once. "The hares appeared at ease," they reported, "hopped around interestedly, and ate a variety of foods. However, a hare appearing normal would suddenly spring into the air in convulsions or sink to the floor in coma. In either case death usually followed from a few minutes to an hour after the onset of symptoms." Most of the diseased hares had the spleen contracted, and many of them showed lesions of the adrenal and thyroid glands. The researchers concluded that the hares were suffering from what they called "shock disease" and what Dr. Hans Selye has called "stress." They further concluded that the original overcrowding in the wild had caused it.

A further insight into the triggering of a stress reaction was given by a study of the hare's companion in the cycle, the ruffed grouse. In this case it was found that the most aggressive male grouse, in captivity, would begin terrorizing the weakest. The results were illuminating: "A bird that has been completely subjugated . . . is subject to attack from every other bird in the enclosure. He has developed an *inferiorism* and usually, unless removed, he remains in a corner until he dies . . . He dies not from mechanical injury nor from starvation, but from some sort of nervous shock, and death is likely to occur within twenty-four hours."

It seems certain that overcrowding somehow produces physical and chemical changes in the animal populations. It also seems certain that these changes curtail the reproductive rate. The yearling hare females simply remain virgin. The litter averages of the other females drop. They bear fewer litters a season, or perhaps only one litter. And of the babies born, three per cent or fewer survive. And in the meantime, the adults themselves are dying off – if not of simple stress, then of diseases and parasites made epidemic by the overcrowding, or of predation by the meat eaters whose own numbers have been swelled. In the depths of a crash, it seems to have disappeared completely.

This much about the ten-year cycle is understood. What is not at all understood is why it happens or why, since it happens, it should happen with such regularity.

What deepens the mystery is the conviction that has been growing in ecological circles that an old truism is false; that nature is not on the side of maximum fertility. Instead, successful populations seem to limit their reproduction, through a whole series of controls such as litter size and number of litters, to precisely what their habitat can support throughout any given year. There is a division of opinion about whether these controls are exercised at the group level or the individual level, but in any case it is agreed that the whole complex environmental web is giving constant signals about its condition and potential to which any component of the environment responds. Thus the moose restrict their numbers in accordance with the year-round carrying capacity of the land – and in years of good food supply produce twins. Ideally, and in a mature and stable environment, with a settled and experienced population, there is never any overcrowding and never a niche left unfilled.

So what makes a particular population suddenly discard its biological controls and start upon reckless breeding? All sorts of triggers have been suggested, from sunspots to lunar cycle. It has even been suggested that the regularity is only apparent, being a statistical effect achieved periodically by the accidental coincidence of random variables such as weather, food-supply and love among the rabbits. But the fur trade figures, and the recent studies in Alberta, make it clear that the regularity is real.

The same Alberta studies are beginning to show one or two teasing correlations. One is a correlation between certain accidents of weather and certain reproductive controls. As the study report expresses it, "Computer facilities were utilized to examine five snowshoe hare population parameters for correlations with twelve weather factors in a wide array of time periods. Intensity of illumination in midwinter, as measured by cloud cover, was highly significantly correlated with the date of onset of breeding the following spring." Early onset of breeding, of course, makes more litters per season possible. Weather, which varies on a regional basis, would certainly go some way towards explaining why the cycling phenomenon is so widespread and well synchronised. But so far it can't explain the regularity. The researchers in Alberta took time off from this work to study the red squirrel populations in two forest areas. What they found was a significant correlation between the squirrel's diet and his fertility. The squirrel's staple food is white-spruce cones. The researchers, with their computers, found a significant correlation between the spruce-cone crop and certain weather conditions – specifically the relative dryness and sunniness of the preceding summer. They concluded, "Our contention that cone production may in this way provide a vehicle through which weather affects squirrel populations was supported. . . ." The white spruce, of course, has its own peaks and crashes in fertility.

None of this is conclusive. But it is suggestive. For the Canadian Shield is a new area, ecologically speaking. It is still being settled by plants. They are fighting it out for space, for elbow-room, for the best sites, for their own kind of poise. And it is still being settled by animals. They, too, are still exploring the territory for its capacities and tolerances. And perhaps they sometimes get the wrong signals; get them too soon or too late; misinterpret them; over-react. Perhaps, sometimes, they just get static. This is not a mature and stable environment.

PART FIVE/ CONSERVATION

18 NATURAL DESTINY

In 1965, amid gathering concern that the planet's tolerances were being strained past the limit, thirty-four of the world's foremost scholars of the environment gathered at Warrenton, Virginia, to probe the current and coming ecological pressures on the North American continent. They met to discuss everything from the statistics of population explosion to the possibility of free-floating houseboat cities; from ways of educating politicians to techniques of climate modification; from the spiritual value of national parks to the projected iron requirements, in short tons, of the U.S. by the year 2000.

They were, that is to say, not just concerned with the preservation of the whooping crane and the wilderness area. This was not one of those dismaying conventions of the good-guys versus the bad-guys that brush aside urgent and legitimate human interests as though man had no right to be around, or at least should have recognized his proper ecological station in life from the start and stayed in the trees.

The debates, as well they might, had an overtone of crisis. The carbon dioxide level was rising. Pollution was suffocating lakes and rivers. Water for industry was growing scarce and some kinds of minerals were running out. The peasantry of Central America were in a land-use trap: "too poor to learn, too ignorant to improve, too frightened to try." Canada was losing its precious hoard of productive land to urban sprawl, and its government was exploiting non-renewable resources for short-term profit. New York City and the whole state of California were already past saving. Eastern Kentucky was ruining its hills to get out coal at two dollars a ton. The physical sciences were simply not up to the job of listing the danger points that might be approaching or already passed. Irreplaceable genetic material was being lost with vanishing species. Delicate natural balances had been destroyed before they'd even been recognized, let alone described for restoration purposes.

In the worried inventory of environmental damage and coming stress, the Canadian Shield, and the tundra and taiga generally, were mentioned a number of times. It was, for example, pointed out in one paper that the margin of ecological safety grows narrower towards the poles. The plants have progressively slower growth rates, and the animals progressively lower birth rates, and because of this both are more vulnerable to interference. One axe-blow in the boreal forest can fell a tree that a hundred years will not replace. A wildfire in the tundra can set vegetation back centuries, and the caribou, having lost their fodder, are threatened.

It was pointed out, too, that the Canadian Shield was too cold, rocky and swampy for current commercial agriculture and that this and other factors made the typical North American industrial-agricultural community an unlikely northern development. "So," asked one scholar, "why even attempt it? In the process of social planning for a continent, certainly one of the alternatives that is always before us is the chance to do nothing at all. Why can't we leave that component part of the continent exactly as it is?" He was raising the most relevant ecological question that can be asked about the Canadian Shield.

For most Canadians, any suggestion that the Shield might be left just as it is verges on national heresy: we have been reared to the notion that northern development would be the cure for everything from the national character to the threat of American takeover – and would make everybody rich to boot. All that radium and gold and iron and nickel and asbestos. All those untouched softwood forests – only a third of them in commercial production as yet. All that untapped hydro-electric power, and reservoirs of pure water. All the fertile virgin lakes for fishing, and the big game for hunting, the finest sport and recreation country in the world awaiting the right developer. And all that unused space. The Russians have five million people living north of the 60th parallel, bustling seaports on the Arctic Ocean and space-age university cities, created by fiat according to the most advanced design, in the remote Siberian taiga. The Swedes have a million people north of Sixty. Even the state of Alaska has 200,000 people. But in the same latitudes, Canada has a mere forty thousand people, and more than half of them are native Indians and Eskimos. Furthermore the assets and resources, and the space, are plainly going to gain in value, giving Canada great leverage by the year 2000. The Americans are already running out of water. By the year 2000 the demand for Canadian softwood is expected to increase three-hundredfold.

The expert dreamers say that about the same time the world's reserves of gold and base metals will be exhausted. Though there is talk of recovering minerals from the sea, other planners say the crisis can only be met by quarrying raw bedrock like that of the Shield and learning to extract every last bit of mineralization from it. And, of course, by the year 2000 the world's population will have doubled again. There are now forty people to every square mile of land surface. In three more decades there will be eighty, and the pressure for living space will be acute.

In spite of Sir Wilfrid Laurier the twentieth century proved elusive; but if Canada would only move in now and do something about her North, she could stake out the twenty-first century for her own. In this context, talk of leaving the North alone seems mischievous or at least silly.

It is generally assumed that northern development means massive northern settlement. Indeed starting with Vilhjalmur Stefansson, most northern visionaries have thought it crucial to convince people that the north is a perfectly splendid place to live: fresh vegetables grown under glass on the spot, tasty Arctic char, fashion clothes from Eaton's catalogue, culture via CBC radio, *Aurora borealis* for the soul, and all that good wholesome fresh air.

As far as most of the Shield is concerned, though, potential settlers have remained less than convinced. Fewer than two million are actual permanent residents of the Shield and of this number 1,750,000 are crowded down along the southern margins in Ontario and Quebec, as close to civilization as they can get. The rest are largely scattered among various mines, lumber camps and company towns somewhere along the Shield perimeter, and the chances are that they had to be bribed with high pay to go there in the first place.

They will drift away again when the booty is exhausted or the economic base collapses. The axiom about remote riches is that they are riches only so long as they can be brought to market at a profit; and given the appalling Shield conditions and the difficulties of transport – and the vagaries of commerce – the profit margin on the resources can disappear overnight. It is certain, for example, that if federal subsidies to the gold mining industry are discontinued, all but two or three of the producing mines will shut down. So there is an historical pattern of ghost towns and abandoned camps within the margins of the Shield, a hit-and-run pattern.

The truth is that most people would just as soon not live on the Shield. Something should be clarified here. It is not precisely a failure of the old pioneer spirit that is keeping the land empty. The kind of frontier that has traditionally lured settlement is an agricultural frontier. It was a chance to be free and self-sufficient by working their own land that attracted the homesteaders to the old west; it attracts them now to Peace River country and the interior valleys of northern British Columbia: it may yet bring them in numbers to the Mackenzie valley.

But the Shield is no place for homesteading. The only real chances for self-sufficiency lie in the trap-line and the hunt, which are scarcely to everyone's taste. So there is no stake in the land, nothing at all, to keep people around any longer than the particular job lasts. And in any case, most people these days prefer to live at human crossroads, where there is lots of two-way traffic, a wide range of services, a chance to shop around, and a bit of action. The mass movement is into the big cities, not out to the spruce and rock and muskeg, among the black flies.

Still, the promise is that the world's need for the Shield resources is going to grow urgent and shrill, very soon. And the American space programme has already shown that man has, or is fast acquiring, the ability to go and live anywhere on the planet (or on the moon for that matter) that he chooses. Furthermore, a specific technology that could change man's relationship to the Shield is already developing. There are new all-terrain, all-weather vehicles, and new instant portable igloos. Techniques of construction on permafrost or muskeg have been worked out. The bulk handling of resources – wood chips or raw ore transported by pipeline – has been proved feasible. The chemical recovery of sour soils for food production is now possible or, if that seems too much trouble, food can be synthesized from sea algae or petroleum. And climate-controlled instant cities, built underground or under plastic domes, are already on the drawing-boards.

And so the visionaries are already planning such instant cities for the Shield. One current northern development plan proposes a new east-west network of roads and railways right across mid-Canada, with a spur running up the Mackenzie valley; a system of "short-cycle" towns, meaning temporary camps to exploit specific resources; and six "population growth centres," meaning permanent cities, designed to support populations of a hundred thousand apiece. Four of the six centres are on the Shield, though not, in truth, all that far on: they're based on existing settlements such as Flin Flon and Thunder Bay. The plan actually manages to skirt the Shield for the most part, but it's clearly expected to be only a beginning.

In this connection an exchange that took place in Moscow in 1967 is of some interest. The scene was the auditorium of Moscow's Architectural Institute, and the occasion was a Soviet academic ritual: the public defence of post-graduate dissertations. A Russian student was offering a thesis on urban planning in the Siberian Arctic.

Now under Stalin the policy of the Soviet planners had been to move industry, and the required manpower, to the sources of fuel, energy and raw materials. And, under Stalin, no Soviet citizen working in the government-run sector of the economy could change jobs without permission. That is an excellent way to settle an unpopular area. However in 1956 the strict labour legislation was slackened and the authorities began to discover that in some years more people were leaving Siberia than arrived there. Investigators found that not even wage incentives were enough to make the people settle down: unsatisfactory housing and inadequate public services were more important factors.

It was in this context that the student offered a thesis on urban planning in the Siberian Arctic. The spirited discussion that followed revolved around the height of buildings and whether the entire town should be covered by a plastic dome or whether structures should be linked by enclosed passages that would keep out the winter cold of forty and fifty degrees below zero.

At this point a middle-aged man from the audience introduced himself as a representative for the State Institute for the Design of Non-ferrous Metals Enterprises and this, as reported by a correspondent for the New York *Times*, is what he said: "I may be out of line but my agency is, so to say, the customer for these town designs. We are the ones who plan the development of those remote mineral sites – gold, tin, diamonds – and we are thus the potential users of these fancy covered settlements. I may be a little blunt, but I feel you are talking in a vacuum. You act as if the principal problem confronting us in those northern latitudes is to make it as cozy as possible for the housewife to go from her home to the grocery store. I would say that you are missing the point. Our problem is not to attract people to settle in those inhospitable areas. If we could help it, we would not want to send anyone there. For one thing, it simply costs too much to maintain people in that environment. Everything has to be flown in – food, fuel, equipment, materials, supplies. We are looking forward not to the accommodation of miners under air-conditioned plastic domes but to increasing mechanization and automation that will reduce the required manpower to the absolute minimum."

Soviet economic planners have now, indeed, adopted a set of policies that call for the movement not of man but of fuel, energy and other raw materials out to areas of natural population concentration.

If the Russians are right, it may be that the correct – indeed the inspired – long-term policy for the Canadian Shield is to get resource-procurement so completely automated that nobody needs to live there. If, instead of efforts to people it, efforts were made to reduce the need for settlement, and if the resource-procurement were wisely regulated and carefully policed, that would go a long way towards keeping most of the Shield as it is.

Men, unfortunately, have crummy habits. Their cities, their industrial complexes, their backyards, and even their recreation grounds are too often saddening and sickening illustrations of the human tendency to befoul without thought or understanding. And where there seems to be superabundance there seems also to be the least thought and the smallest effort at understanding.

So, wherever there are people on the Shield now, the blight has already begun to show. Swimming had to be banned in the Lake of Two Rivers, in Algonquin Park, in 1969, because the raw human waste from 2,000 campers a day had polluted the water.

During the Sixties, sport fishing was opened up in a big way on Great Slave Lake, Great Bear Lake and, farther north on the tundra, on Tree River. The water in these sub-arctic Shield lakes is so cold and low in nutrients that the lake trout grow very slowly, and spawn only once every three years. But these are virgin waters and even a novice can take a thousand pounds of fish in a day. So all summer rich American and Canadian anglers fly in on private planes or charter flights for the sport. The trouble is they are not only gluttonous but they handle the fish so carelessly – grabbing fistfulls by the gills – that one government official estimates that ninety-five to ninety-nine per cent of the fish

Sudbury smeltering plants, spewing a million tons of sulphur dioxide a year, have killed most vegetation within 400 square miles.

they throw back can't possibly survive. In 1963, seven hundred anglers on Great Bear Lake managed to catch and destroy half a million pounds of lake trout.

In the boreal forest, forestry experts have begun to notice that the majority of burns tend to occur along the canoe routes.

Near Sioux Lookout, the Ontario Department of Lands and Forests developed a recreation area as a tourist attraction and they stocked the lake with speckled trout for ten years. The sportsmen cut and hacked at living trees around the margins for firewood, strew beer cans and garbage everywhere and ended by burning out the entire area.

And then there is Sudbury. Three Sudbury plants, spewing a million tons of sulphur dioxide a year, have killed all vegetation within an area of four hundred square miles. Beyond, over an area of 1670 square miles, there is detectable vegetation damage.

Rain picks up the acidity from the polluted air, and the rain in the Sudbury area is now so acidic that in at least one lake,

thirty-five miles southeast of Sudbury, the fish have virtually disappeared since 1967. The biologist who discovered this has described the effect on fish of increased acid in their environment: "The fish first of all reduce their growth, then they reduce and stop reproduction . . . and after they stop their reproduction they stop feeding and become very susceptible to diseases and eventually die."

In the same way some smeltering plants have killed all vegetation downwind, producing an eerie landscape of dead sticks.

And there are other kinds of pollution, subtler and even more savage offences. Among them must be numbered the planned company towns like Thompson, Manitoba, where the imported white workers live in spacious rows of family homes and shop in gleaming shopping centres, while the Indians and Métis make shift in shanties beyond the tracks. There are native ghettoes, slums, like these just outside every settlement on the Shield.

Float planes, because they can land on water, are often the only means by which many far-northern points can receive needed supplies.

Yet the blight is still only on the perimeters, or on isolated and identifiable patches not far within them. The rest of the Shield still lies almost unmolested. Much of it has never been seen by white men at ground level, and there are undoubtedly parts, given its staggering size and appalling terrain, that haven't been seen by Indians or Eskimos either. The muskeg is unvisited. A million square miles of forest are virtually intact. The lakes are unpolluted and the rivers sparkle. Beyond the treeline, the tundra and the rock desert stretch off empty to the north, so unpopular that only the necessities of wartime reconnaissance brought a plane at last to discover the vast New Quebec crater in Ungava.

The Great Lakes-St. Lawrence forest may be overrun, but the taiga and tundra of the Shield are just what the conservationists keep ordering. Two million square miles of spruce and moss and lichen breathe out oxygen to counteract the mounting CO_2 in the atmosphere. The resident animal life has been left alone to work out its own evolutionary destiny. Only the migratory species risk the human gauntlet. During one of their periodic mass excursions from the tundra, some five thousand snowy owls were shot by Canadian and American hunters in the course of a season; a Boston taxidermist was so swamped with orders that he had to cable Europe for an extra 250 pairs of glass owls' eyes. Serious scientists, if they are so minded, can go into the Shield and study undisturbed spruce-lichen woodland, the formation of string bogs, the disposition of warbler niches, or the biting rates of the black fly on humid days, without building the effects of massive human interference into their research calculations.

Here is a wilderness so primal that a mere mortal can grow frightened and respectful alone in the heart of the Shield, and that is perhaps no very bad reminder these days. But aside from the superstitious, or the research-minded, no one wants to go there. And it may be that no one needs to go there, not even to make Canada rich. And so, as the scholar at the Warrenton, Virginia, conference asked, "Why even attempt it?" Why not leave it as it is – waste space, perhaps, but perhaps also a peace-offering?

The answer, of course, is that it can't be done. Man didn't stay in the trees. He came down to the clearings, and invented the wheel, and built cities, and split atoms and, like the varying hare in the abnormal season, took to unbridled breeding. And now no part of the planet, however it might seem, is any longer in a state of nature.

It is not just that a man may live in Minneapolis and yet destroy the wildlife balance of the tundra: already the helicopter has put the polar bear on the list of threatened species.

It is not just that financiers from three countries can meet in New York and agree to turn off one of the world's most spectacular waterfalls like a tap. Their Churchill Falls power development in Labrador will flood a good portion of the interior of Labrador creating a lake fully a third the size of Lake Ontario and upsetting environmental patterns in a way that can only be guessed at.

It is not just that the continental thirst for fresh water is already spawning schemes like the recent one to dam Hudson Bay, pump out the salt water and use the basin as a freshwater reservoir for the streams and rivers in the Hudson Bay drainage area. The proponent of the scheme, a former Ontario civil servant, says he hopes that nuclear-powered pumps could be developed to carry out the scheme, because the heat produced as a by-product could be used to keep the bay ice-free and navigable all year round. The ecological crisis has made it clear how mischievous such schemes can be, and how subtle and far-reaching their effects.

And it is not even that the time of outright demands on Canada to accommodate the world's overflow population may be fast approaching.

All these things suggest that the Shield cannot just be left alone, or its future trusted to luck. They suggest that planning for it should not be postponed, no matter how tempting it is to think of the Shield as largely safe for the moment.

But they are not the real and overriding reasons for action. Doing nothing at all in the Shield is unthinkable not because of the future but because of the past. Far from being safe for the moment, the Shield as an ecosystem was damaged long ago – and damaged in a way that demands repair and redress. The debt is overdue. Some years ago a sociologist working for the Canadian government published a study on the Eskimos who live west of Hudson Bay. It seemed that twenty or twenty-five years before there had been 386 inhabitants supporting themselves, more or less naturally, on the 100,000 square miles of the tundra. Twenty years later there were 368 inhabitants. The message was clear: the ecosystem was full. This approximate number of Eskimos – somewhere just under four hundred – was the carrying capacity of the tundra for native man living as part of the natural system.

There are, of course, no Eskimos living entirely off the land these days. White man, western man, came and offered money for furs. In order to get furs the Eskimo had to travel a great deal more than before, which meant he had to have three times the number of dogs and three times the amount of food and so the delicate balance between man and his environment was wrecked. The Eskimos have given up the nomad life. They live in shacks, in little settlements on the coast now, and they go in debt to buy snowmobiles.

And in the same way white men, western men, we Canadians, have disinherited the Indians and the Métis, wrecked the primeval community and given them instead – rural slums on the Shield. Almost all the tiny population of Shield taiga and Shield tundra is native. Leaving the Shield as it is, leaving it to unplanned fate, means bucking not just an ecological challenge but a humanitarian one.

The clock cannot be turned back. There is no way to return the Shield – or any other part of the world – to a state of nature. But it cannot be left as it is. To do so means disowning an ecological debt – and a moral duty.

When the scholar at the Warrenton conference asked why the Shield couldn't just be left alone, a colleague reminded him of the native peoples and answered him bluntly: "We can't . . . we are into it up to our necks."

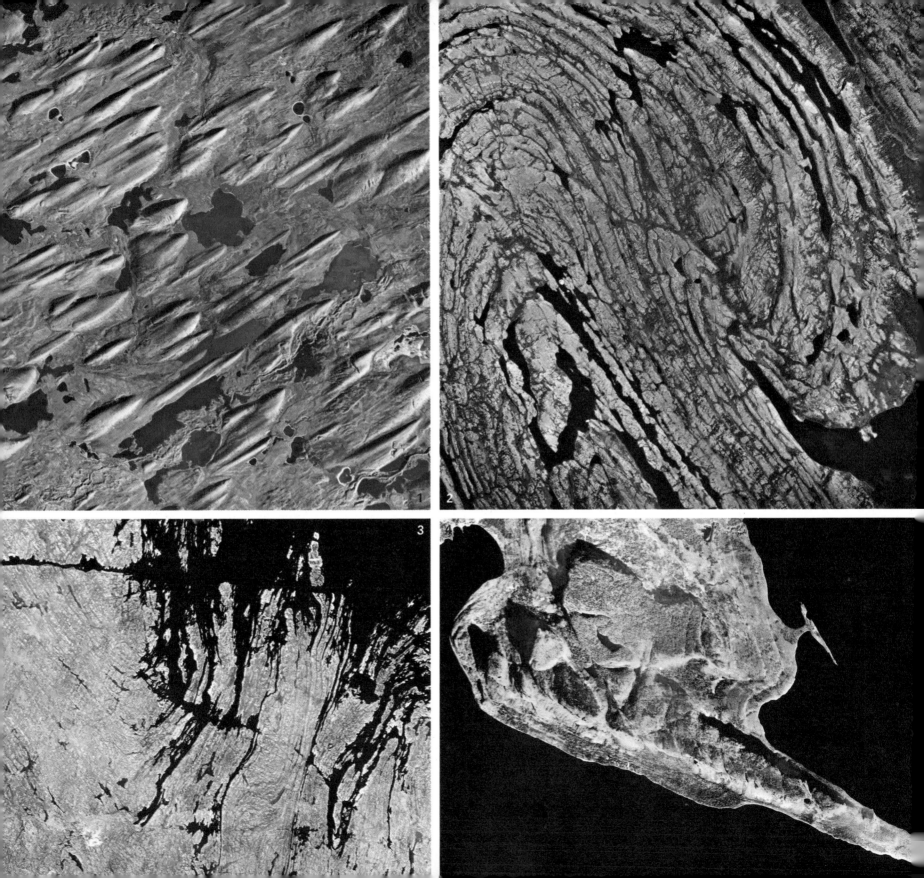

Patterns from the air

Because erosion has etched the natural pattern of folded and faulted rocks into bold relief, many of the events that affected the Precambrian Shield can be observed and interpreted by means of air photographs. The softer rocks are eroded to form lowlands and valleys while the harder ones remain as ridges. The scars of glaciation are reflected by the landforms and the character of the drainage pattern.

1. Drumlins – a glacial landform at Black Lake, Saskatchewan.

2. Complex folding – in igneous and sedimentary rocks near Tait Lake, Que.

3. Broad fold – in schists and gneisses in northeast Georgian Bay, Ontario.

4. The Sleeping Giant – an eroded diabase sill at Thunder Bay, Ontario.

5. The Ungava Crater – a meteorite crater near Ungava Bay, Quebec.

Overleaf:
The MacDonald Lake Fault, N.W.T., at the east end of Great Slave Lake, is one of the very large faults that occur throughout the Precambrian Shield. This particular fault has been traced for several hundred miles through the rock.

GEOLOGIC TIME SCALE

TIME	ERA	PERIOD	EPOCH	THE ASCENT OF LIFE:
	CENOZOIC	QUATERNARY	PLEISTOCENE	
		TERTIARY	PLIOCENE	
			MIOCENE	
			OLIGOCENE	
50			EOCENE	
			PALEOCENE	
100	MESOZOIC	CRETACEOUS	UPPER	
			LOWER	
150		JURASSIC	UPPER	
			MIDDLE	
			LOWER	
200		TRIASSIC	UPPER	
			MIDDLE	
			LOWER	
250	PALAEOZOIC	PERMIAN	UPPER	
			MIDDLE	
			LOWER	
300		PENNSYLVANIAN		
350		MISSISSIPPIAN		
		DEVONIAN	UPPER	
			MIDDLE	
400			LOWER	
		SILURIAN		
450		ORDOVICIAN	UPPER	
			MIDDLE	
			LOWER	
500		CAMBRIAN	UPPER	
550			MIDDLE	
			LOWER	

MILLIONS OF YEARS

THE ASCENT OF LIFE: 1, *protozoan;* 2, *jellyfish;* 3, *crinoid;* 4, *cephalopod;* 5, *climatius;* 6, *shark;* 7, *brachiopod;* 8, *seed fern;* 9, *dimetrodon;* 10, *brontosaurus;* 11, *plesiosaur;* 12, *tyrannosaurus;* 13, *taeniolabis;* 14, *diatryma;* 15, *hyracotherium;* 16, *brontotherium;* 17, *oxydactylus;* 18, *pliohippus;* 19, *mastodon;* 20, *man.*

SHORT LIST OF ROCKS, PLANTS AND ANIMALS

The lists on the following pages have been compiled as a basic guide for amateur naturalists intending to explore the wealth of natural history of the Canadian Shield. These selected summaries cannot possibly cover all species — there are many thousands of insects alone — but an attempt has been made to include the common life forms and the natural phenomena peculiar to this region. Readers should find it useful to study the lists touching on their sphere of interest, checking off items they have observed during field trips. Those wishing to extend their search will find an extensive Bibliography on pages 153-5; references listed there contain more detailed information on specific subjects.

ROCKS

Those listed are the most interesting and typical to be found in the locations named.

YELLOWKNIFE, N.W.T.
Almandite
Amethyst
Andalusite
Apatite
Arsenopyrite
Bismuthinite
Cassiterite
Clinozoisite
Columbite
Cordierite
Fluorite
Gahnite
Graphite
Lazulite
Molybdenite
Native copper
Native gold
Perthite

Quartz
Scheelite
Sillimanite
Sodalite
Spinel
Stibnite
Tantalite
Tetrahedrite
Titanite
Tourmaline
Vesuvianite
Wollastonite

BERNIC LAKE, MANITOBA
Amblygonite
Apatite
Beryl
Garnet
Lepidolite
Microcline feldspar
Monazite
Petalite
Rose quartz
Spodumene
Topaz
Tourmaline

THUNDER BAY, ONTARIO
Agate
Amethyst
Apatite
Argentite
Barite
Calcite
Chalcedony
Chalcopyrite
Danburnite
Datolite
Fluorite
Galena
Hematite
Jasper
Magnetite
Marcasite
Native silver
Pectolite
Prenite
Siderite
Smoky quartz
Sphalerite

SAULT STE. MARIE, ONTARIO
Agate

Bornite
Calcite
Chalcedony
Chalcocite
Chalcopyrite
Chlorite
Epidote
Galena
Hematite
Jasper
Laumonite
Native copper
Prenite
Pyrite
Sphalerite

SUDBURY, ONTARIO
Biotite
Chalcopyrite
Galena
Garnet
Kyanite
Microcline feldspar
Pentlandite
Phlogopite
Pyrite

Pyrrhotite
Sillimanite
Sphalerite
Sperrylite

BANCROFT, ONTARIO
Albite
Allanite
Anatase
Apatite
Betafite
Biotite
Calcite
Cancrinite
Corundum
Diopside
Ellsworthite
Epidote
Fluorite
Hematite
Hornblende
Hydronepheline
Ilmenite
Magnetite
Microcline feldspar
Molybdenite
Nepheline
Peristerite
Phlogopite
Pyrite
Pyrochlore
Pyroxene
Rose quartz
Scapolite
Sodalite
Smoky quartz
Thorite
Titanite
Tourmaline
Uraninite
Uranophane
Uranothorite
Zircon

MADOC, ONTARIO
Actinolite
Amphibole
Apatite

Arsenopyrite
Barite
Calcite
Celestite
Chalcocite
Chlorite
Fluorite
Garnet
Pyrite
Quartz
Rutile
Talc
Tourmaline
Tremolite

KINGSTON, ONTARIO
Actinolite
Apatite
Augite
Biotite
Calcite
Datolite
Diopside
Enstatite
Garnet
Graphite
Hematite
Hornblende
Magnetite
Peristerite
Phlogopite
Pyrite
Quartz
Scapolite
Tourmaline
Tremolite

HULL, QUEBEC
Albite
Apatite
Barite
Brucite
Calcite
Celestite
Chlorite
Chrysotile asbestos
Diopside
Fluorite

Forsterite
Garnet
Graphite
Hematite
Hornblende
Jasper
Magnetite
Molybdenite
Muscovite
Phlogopite
Pyrite
Quartz
Rutile
Scapolite
Serpentine
Sphalerite
Spinel
Talc
Titanite
Tourmaline
Tremolite
Vesuvianite
Wilsonite

LAC ST. JEAN, QUEBEC
Amazonite
Beryl
Cleavlandite
Ilmenite
Labradorite
Magnetite
Muscovite
Pyrite
Pyrrhotite
Quartz
Topaz

PLANTS

LICHENS
Nephroma arcticum
Nephroma bellum
Peltigera aphthosa
Peltigera pulverulenta
Lecidea cinereoatra
Lecidea dicksonii
Lecidea flavocaerulescens

Lecidea subsorediza
Mycoblastus sanguinarius
Rhizocarpon jemtlandicum
Rhizocarpon geographicum
Cladonia alpestris

Cladonia rangiferina
Cladonia coccifera
Cladonia uncialis
Cladonia cornuta
Cladonia digitata
Cladonia pleurota
Cladonia cholrophaea
Cladonia polydactyla
Cladonia subrangiformis
Stereocaulon paschale
Actinogyra mühlenbergii
Umbilicaria hyperborea
Lecanora arctica
Lecanora polytropa
Icmadophila ericetorum
Parmeliopsis ambigua
Parmeliopsis hyperopta
Parmelia centrifuga
Parmelia sulcata
Parmelia incurva
Cetraria nivalis
Cetraria nigricascens
Cetraria crispa
Cetraria pinastri
Cetraria ciliaris
Alectoria altaica
Alectoria jubata
Rinodina annulata

MOSSES
Andreaea rupestris
Atrichum undulatum
Polytrichum commune
Polytrichum juniperinum

Dicranum elongatum
Dicranum bergeri
Dicranum fuscens
Dicranum groenlandicum
Dicranum mühlenbergii
Grimmia affinis
Grimmia alpicola
Hedwigia ciliata
Aulacomnium palustre
Paludella squarrosa
Leptobryum pyriforme
Pohlia cruda

Pohlia nutans
Mnium affine
Mnium andrewsianum
Calliergon cordifolium
Campylium stellatum
Drepanocladus exannulatus
Drepanocladus fluitans
Hygrohypnum alpestre
Plagiothecium denticulatum
Ptilium crista-castrensis
Pleurozium schreberi
Hypnum lindbergii
Hylocomium splendens
Fontinalis nitida
Sphagnum cuspidatum
Sphagnum girgensohnii
Sphagnum fuscum
Sphagnum lindbergii
Sphagnum recurvum
Sphagnum robustum
Sphagnum teres
Sphagnum balticum
Sphagnum riparium

HORSETAILS
Common horsetail
Equisetum arvense

Woodland horsetail
Equisetum sylvaticum
Marsh horsetail
Equisetum palustre
Water horsetail
Equisetum fluviatile
Variegated horsetail
Equisetum variegatum
CLUBMOSSES
Shining clubmoss
Lycopodium lucidulum
Bog clubmoss
Lycopodium inundatum
Bristly clubmoss
Lycopodium annotinum

Running clubmoss
Lycopodium clavatum
Tree clubmoss
Lycopodium obscurum
Ground-cedar
Lycopodium tristachyum
FERNS
Royal fern
Osmunda regalis
Interrupted fern
Osmunda claytonia
Cinnamon fern
Osmunda cinnamomea
Fragrant woodsia
Woodsia ilvensis
Fragile fern
Cystopteris fragilis
Ostrich fern
Pteretis pennsylvanica
Sensitive fern
Onoclea sensibilis
Marsh fern
Dryopteris noveboracensis
Oak fern
Dryopteris disjuncta
Beech fern
Dryopteris phegopteris
Wood fern
Dryopteris spinulosa

Marginal shield fern
Dryopteris marginalis
Fragrant cliff fern
Dryopteris fragrans
Hay-scented fern
Dennstaedtia punctilobula
Silvery spleenwort
Athyrium thelypterioides
Lady fern
Athyrium felix-femina
Maidenhair fern
Adiantum pedatum
Bracken fern
Pteridium aquilinum
Rock polypody
Polypodium virginianum

SEED PLANTS
Common cat-tail
Typha latifolia
Bur-reed
Sparganium angustifolium
Leafy pondweed
Potamogeton foliosus
Floating pondweed
Potamogeton epihydrus
Swimming pondweed
Potamogeton natans
Crested arrowhead
Sagittaria cristata
Duck-potato
Sagittaria latifolia
Brome-grass
Bromus commutatus
Rattlesnake grass
Glyceria canadensis
Canada bluegrass
Poa compressa
Long-haired speargrass
Poa longipila
Pasture speargrass
Poa saltuensis

Rye-grass
Lolium perenne
Squirrel-tail grass
Hordeum jubatum
Blue-joint grass
Calamagrostis canadensis
Redtop bentgrass
Agrostis alba
Hairgrass
Abrostis scabra
Three-way sedge
Duluchium arundinaceum
Spike-rush
Eleocharis smallii
Swaying rush
Scirpus subterminalis
Hare's-tail cottongrass
Eriophorum spissum
Cottongrass
Eriophorum viridi-carinatum
Tawny cottongrass
Eriophorum virginicum
Three-seeded sedge
Carex trisperma

Jack-in-the-pulpit
Arisaema atrorubens

Wild calla-lily
Calla palustris
Water flaxseed
Spirodela polyrhiza
Yellow-eyed grass
Xyris montana
Duckgrass
Eriocaylon septangulare
Pickeralweed
Pontederia cordata
Slender rush
Juncus tenuis
Soft rush
Juncus effusus
Short-tailed rush
Juncus brevicaudatus
Yellow adder's-tongue
Erythronium americanum

Yellow clintonia
Clintonia borealis
Solomon's zigzag
Smilacina racemosa
False solomon's seal
Smilacina stellata
Threeleaf smilacina
Smilacina trifolia
False lily-of-the-valley
Maianthemum canadense
Twisted stalk
Streptopus roseus
Solomon's seal
Polygonatum pubescens
Indian cucumber
Medeola virginiana
Nodding trillium
Trillium cernuum
Purple trillium
Trillium erectum
White trillium
Trillium grandiflorum
Painted trillium
Trillium undulatum
Blue-eyed grass
Sisyrinchium mucronatum
Blue iris
Iris versicolor
Common lady's slipper
Cypripedium acaule
Yellow lady's slipper
Cypripedium calceolus
Frog orchid
Habenaria viridis
Round-leaved orchid
Habenaria orbiculata
Blunt-leaf orchid
Habenaria obtusata
Grass-pink
Calopogon pulchellus
Northern slender ladies'
    tresses
Spiranthes lacera

Rattlesnake plantain
Goodyera repens
Downy rattlesnake plantain
Goodyera pubescens
Heartleaf twayblade
Listera cordata
Spotted coral-root
Corallorhiza maculata
Early coral-root
Corallorhiza trifida
Adder's mouth
Malaxis unifolia
Green adder's mouth
Malaxis unifolia
Nettle
Urtica viridis
Stinging nettle
Urtica dioica
Yellow dock
Rumex crispus
Sheep-sorrel
Rumex acetosella
Common ladies' tresses
Spiranthes cernua

Hooded ladies' tresses
Spiranthes romanzoffiana
Knotweed
Polygonum aviculare
Water smartweed
Polygonum amphibium
Arrow-leaved tearthumb
Polygonum sagittatum
Black bindweed
Polygonum convolvulus
Green amaranth
Amaranthus retroflexus
Spring-beauty
Claytonia caroliniana
Common chickweed
Stellaria media
Common stitchwort
Stellaria graminea

White campion
Lychnis alba
Bladder-campion
Silene cucubalus
Sticky cockle
Silene noctiflora
Yellow cress
Rorippa islandica
Rock cress
Arabis laevigata
Common winter cress
Barbarea orthoceras
Bullhead lily
Nuphar variegatum
Fragrant water-lily
Nymphaea odorata
Water-shield
Brassenia schreberi
Kidneyleaf buttercup
Ranunculus avortivus
Buttercup
Ranunculus recurvatus
Bristly crowfoot
Ranunculus pensylvanicus
Macoun's buttercup
Ranunculus macounii
Creeping-buttercup
Ranunculus repens
Tall meadow-rue
Thalictrum polygamum
Anemone
Anemone canadensis

Goldthread
Coptis groenlandica
Red baneberry
Actaea rubra
White baneberry
Actaea pachypoda
Dutchman's breeches
Dicentra cucullaria
Pale corydalis
Corydalis sempervirens

Charlock
Brassica kaber
Pitcher-plant
Sarracenia purpurea
Sundew
Drosera intermedia
Round-leaved sundew
Drosera rotundifolia
Mossy stonecrop
Sedum acre
Early saxifrage
Saxifraga virginiensis
Bishop's-cap
Mitella nuda
Common strawberry
Fragaria virginiana
Woodland strawberry
Fragaria vesca
Barren strawberry
Waldsteinia fragarioides
Three-toothed cinquefoil
Potentilla tridentata
Marsh cinquefoil
Potentilla palustris
Silvery cinquefoil
Potentilla argentea
Old-field cinquefoil
Potentilla simplex
False violet
Dalibarda repens
Cocklebur
Agrimonia parviflora
Yellow avens
Geum aleppicum
Common wood-sorrel
Oxalis montana
Wood-sorrel
Oxalis filipes
Pain d'oiseau
Oxalis europea
Foamflower
Tiarella cordifolia

Cranesbill
Geranium bicknellii

Flowering wintergreen
Polygala paucifolia

Water starwort
Callitriche palustris

Spotted touch-me-not
Impatiens capensis

Common mallow
Malva neglecta

Musk-mallow
Malva moschata

Common St. John's-wort
Hypericum perforatum

Marsh St. John's-wort
Hypericum virginicum

Blue violet
Viola cucullata

Northern blue violet
Viola septentrionalis

Alpine marsh violet
Viola palustris

Kidneyleaf violet
Viola renifolia

Lance-leaved violet
Viola lanceolata

Northern white violet
Viola pallens

Spiked loosestrife
Lythrum salicaria

Fireweed
Epilobium angustifolium

Enchanter's nightshade
Circaia alpina

Water milfoil
Myriophyllum exalbescens

Wild sarsaparilla
Aralia nudicaulis

Black snakeroot
Sanicula marilandica

Anise-root
Osmorhiza longistylis

Water-hemlock
Cicuta bulbifera

Wild carrot
Daucus carota

Bunchberry
Cornus canadensis

One-sided wintergreen
Pyrola secunda

Wild lily-of-the-valley
Pyrola elliptica

Indian-pipe
Monotropa uniflora

Yellow loosestrife
Lysimachia terrestris

Moneywort
Lysimachia nummularia

Tufted loosestrife
Lysimachia thyrsiflora

Star flower
Trientalis borealis

Closed gentian
Gentiana linearis

Spreading dogbane
Apocynum androsaemifolium

Swamp-milkweed
Asclepias incarnata

Wild morning-glory
Convolvulus sepium

Blueweed
Echium vulgare

Northern wild comfrey
Cynoglossum boreale

Blue vervain
Verbena hastata

Bog-rosemary
Andromeda glaucophylla

Leather-leaf
Chamaedaphne calyculata

Bearberry
Arctostaphylos uva-ursi

Creeping snowberry
Gaultheria hispidula

Wintergreen
Gaultheria procumbens

Cowberry
Vaccinium vitis-idaea

Small cranberry
Vaccinium oxycoccos

Bogbean
Menyanthes trifoliata

Sweet-scented bedstraw
Galium triflorum

Northern bedstraw
Galium boreale

Marsh bedstraw
Galium palustre

Marsh-bellflower
Campanula aparinoides

Mad-dog skullcap
Scutellaria lateriflora

Common skullcap
Scutellaria epilobiifolia

Heal-all
Prunella vulgaris

False dragonhead
Physostegia parviflora

Bugleweed
Lycopus uniflorus

Wild mint
Mentha arvensis

Common mullein
Verbascum thapsus

Foxglove
Digitalis purpurea

Marsh speedwell
Veronica scutellata

Corn speedwell
Veronica arvensis

Cow-wheat
Melampyrum lineare

Beech-drops
Epifagus virginiana

Purple bladderwort
Utricularia purpurea

Common bladderwort
Utricularia vulgaris

Spring-cleavers
Galium aparine

Cardinal-flower
Lobelia cardinalis

Indian tobacco
Lobelia inflata

Water lobelia
Lobelia dortmanna

Hobble-bush
Viburnum alnifolium

High-bush cranberry
Viburnum trilobum

Snowberry
Symphoricarpos albus

Joe-pye-weed
Eupatorium maculatum

Boneset
Eupatorium perfoliatum

Goldenrod
Solidago puberula

Canadian goldenrod
Solidago canadensis

Bog goldenrod
Solidago humilis

Grassleaf goldenrod
Solidago graminifolia

Bigleaf aster
Aster macrophyllus

Aster
Aster pilosus

Bog-aster
Aster nemoralis

Robin's plantain
Erigeron pulchellus

Fleabane
Erigeron philadelphicus

Daisy fleabane
Erigeron annuus

Horse-weed
Erigeron canadensis

Canada pussy-toes
Antennaria canadensis

Pearly-everlasting
Anaphalis margaritacea

Black-eyed susan
Rudbeckia serotina

Orange hawkweed
Hieracium aurantiacum

SHRUBS

Buffalo-berry
Shepherdia canadensis

Shrubby cinquefoil
Potentilla fruticosa

Black honeysuckle
Lonicera involucrata
Climbing honeysuckle
Lonicera dioica
Dwarf juniper
Juniperus communis

Serviceberry
Amelanchier alnifolia
Bartram's serviceberry
Amelanchier bartramiana
Bitter current
Ribes triste
Bristly current
Ribes lacustre
Skunk current
Ribes glandulosum
Squashberry
Viburnum edule
Witherod viburnum
Viburnum cassinoides
Red-osier dogwood
Cornus stolonifera
Wild red raspberry
Rubus idaeus
Bog laurel
Kalmia polifolia
Sheep laurel
Kalmia angustifolia
Dwarf birch
Betula glandulosa
Bearberry willow
Salix uva-ursi
Beaked willow
Salix Bebbiana
Pussy willow
Salix discolor

TREES

Eastern white pine
Pinus strobus
Red pine
Pinus resinosa

Jack pine
Pinus banksiana
Tamarack
Larix laricina
White spruce
Picea glauca
Black spruce
Picea mariana
Eastern hemlock
Tsuga canadensis
Balsam fir
Abies balsamea
Eastern white cedar
Thuja occidentalis
Balsam poplar
Populus balsamifera
White birch
Betula papyrifera

Speckled alder
Alnus rugosa
Green alder
Alnus crisoa
Beech
Fagus grandifolia
White elm
Ulmus americana
Slippery elm
Ulmus rubra
Showy mountain ash
Sorbus decora
American mountain ash
Sorbus americana
Black cherry
Prunus serotina
Pin cherry
Prunus pensylvanica
Choke cherry
Prunus virginiana
Mountain maple
Acer spicatum
Black ash
Fraxinus nigra

ANIMALS

FRESHWATER FISH

Lake sturgeon
Acipenser fulvescens
Alpine char
Salvelinus alpinus
Brook trout
Salvelinus fontinalis
Lake trout
Salvelinus namaycush

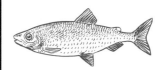

Lake whitefish
Coregonus clupeaformis
Round whitefish
Prosopium cylindraceum
Nipigon cisco
Coregonus nipigon
Shortnose cisco
Coregonus reghardi
Shortjaw cisco
Coregonus zenithicus
Bloater
Coregonus hoyi
Blackfin cisco
Coregonus nigripinnis
Arctic grayling
Thymallus arcticus
Goldeye
Hiodon alosoides
Central mudminnow
Umbra limi
Northern pike
Esox lucius
Muskellunge
Esox masquinongy
Quillback carpsucker
Carpiodes cyprinus
White sucker
Catostomus commersoni
Longnose sucker
Catostomus catostomus
Silver redhorse
Moxostoma anisurum

Lake chub
Couesius plumbeus
Creek chub
Semotilus atromaculatus
Redbelly dace
Chrosomus eos
Finescale dace
Chrosomus neogaeus
Golden shiner
Notemigonus crysoleucas
Fathead minnow
Pimephales promelas
Bluntnose minnow
Pimephales notatus
Emerald shiner
Notropis atherinoides
Spottail shiner
Notropis hudsonius
Blacknose shiner
Notropis heterolepis
Longnose dace
Rhinichthys cataractae
Mimic shiner
Notropis voucellus
Brown bullhead
Ictaluras nebulosus
Channel catfish
Ictalurus punctatus
Burbot
Lota lota

Brook stickleback
Culaea inconstans
Ninespine stickleback
Pungitius pungitius
Trout-perch
Percopsis omiscomaycus
Smallmouth bass
Micropterus dolomieui
Yellow walleye
Stizostedion vitreum vitreum
Sauger
Stizostedion canadense

Yellow perch
Perca flavescens
River darter
Percina shumardi
Logperch
Percina caprodes
Johnny darter
Etheostoma nigrum
Iowa darter
Etheostoma exile
Mottled sculpin
Cottus bairdi
Slimy sculpin
Cottus cognatus
Spoonhead sculpin
Cottus ricei
Deepwater sculpin
Myoxocephalus quadricornis
   thompsoni

AMPHIBIANS

Common toad
Bufo americanus
Hudson Bay toad
Bufo americanus copei
Mink frog
Rana septentrionalis
Wood frog
Rana sylvatica

Boreal frog
Pseudacris triseriata
Leopard frog
Rana pipiens pipiens
Northern spring peeper
Hyla crucifer

INSECTS

Grasshopper
Melanpolus borealis
Damsel fly
Coenagrion resolutum

Dragon fly
Somatochlora franklini
Stone fly
Pteronarcys dorsata
Shore bug
Chiloxanthus stellata
Water strider
Gerris pingreensis
Caddis fly
Apatania zonella
Pearly eye
Lethe portlandia
Eyed brown
Lethe eurydice
Little wood stayr
Euptychia cymela

Northern wood nymph
Cercyonis pegala
Macoun's Arctic
Oeneis macounii
Chryxus Arctic
Oeneis chryxus
Jutta Arctic
Oeneis jutta
Monarch
Danaus plexippus
Variegated fritillary
Euptoieta claudia
Atlantis fritillary
Speyeria atlantis
Great spangled fritillary
Speyeria cybele
Aphrodite fritillary
Speyeria aphrodite
Silver-bordered fritillary
Boloria selene
Bog fritillary
Boloria eunomia
Silvery checkerspot
Melitaea harrisii
Pearl crescent
Phyciodes tharos

Tawny crescent
Phyciodes batesii
Violet tip
Polygonia interrogationis
Comma
Polygonia comma
Green comma
Polygonia faunus
Grey comma
Polygonia progne
Hoary comma
Polygonia gracilis
Compton tortoise shell
Nymphalis l-album j-album
Mourning cloak
Nymphalis antiopa
American tortoise shell
Nymphalis milberti
Red admiral
Vanessa cardui
American painted lady
Vanessa virginiensis
White admiral
Limenitis arthemis
Viceroy
Limenitis archippus
Coral hairstreak
Strymon titus
Striped hairstreak
Strymon liparops
Early hairstreak
Erora laeta
Brown elfin
Incisalia augustinius
Hoary elfin
Incisalia polios
Pine elfin
Incisalia niphon
Harvester
Feniseca tarquinius
American copper
Lycaena epixanthe
Eastern tailed blue
Everes comyntas
Saepiolus blue
Plebeius saepolus
Silvery blue
Glaucopsyche lydamus
Spring azure
Celastrine pseudargiolus
Northern azure
Celastrina lucia
Tiger swallowtail
Papilio glaucus

Common sulphur
Colia philodice
Orange sulphur
Colias eurytheme
Hybrid sulphur
Colias philodice
Pink-edged sulphur
Colias interior
Little sulphur
Eurema lisa
Mustard white
Pieris napi
Cabbage white
Pieris rapae

Northern cloudy wing
Thorybes pylades
Dreamy dusky wing
Erynnis icelus
Juvenal's dusky wing
Erynnis juvenalis
Persius dusky wing
Erynnis persius
Arctic skipper
Carterocephalus palaemon
Least skipper
Ancyloxipha numitor
European skipper
Thymelicus lineola
Leonardus skipper
Hesperia leonardus
Laurentian skipper
Hesperia comma
Pocahontas skipper
Poanes hobomok var.
   pocahontas
Two-spotted skipper
Atrytone ruricola
Roadside skipper
Amblyscirtes vialis
Pepper and salt skipper
Amblyscirtes hegon

Red-disked alpine
Erebia discoidalis
Disa alpine
Erebia disa
Purple lesser fritillary
Bolaria titania
Saga fritillary
Bolaria frigga
Satyr angle-wing
Polygonia satyrus
Water beetle
Agabus moestus
Ground beetle
Amara alpina
Flat-headed wood borer
Melanophila acuminata
Ground beetle
Carabus maeander
Longhorned beetle
Monochamus scutellatus
Red turnip beetle
Entomoscellis americana
Hover fly
Helophilus borealis
Dungfly
Scatopaga multisetosa
Blowfly
Phormia terraenovae
Crane fly
Tipula arctica
Bot fly
Cephenemyia trompi
Warble fly
Oedemagena tarandi
Tachinid fly
Spoggosia gelida
Blowfly
Lucilia illustris
Horsefly
Tabanus affinis
Deer fly
Chrysops excitans
Muscoid fly
Graphomyia idessa
Mosquito
Aedes communis
Aedes excrucians
Aedes impiger
Aedes nigripes
Aedes punctor
Blackfly
Prosimulum fuscum
Prosimulum mixtum
Prosimulum gibsoni

Prosimulum hirtipes
Cnephia eremites
Cnephia invenusta
Cnephia mutata
Cnephia abdita
Simulum parnassum
Simulum euryaminiculum

Simulum venustum
Simulum vittatum
Simulum decorum
Simulum rugglesi
Simulum croxtoni
Simulum damnosum
Simulum latipes
Simulum ureacadeum

BIRDS

Only birds nesting in the area are listed

Common loon
Gavia immer
Red-necked grebe
Podiceps grisegena
Horned grebe
Podiceps auritus
Double-crested cormorant
Phalacrocorax auritus
Great blue heron
Ardea herodias
American bittern
Botaurus lentiginosus
Canada goose
Branta canadensis
Mallard
Anas platyrhynchos
Black duck
Anas rubripes
Pintail
Anas acuta
Green-winged teal
Anas carolinensis
Blue-winged teal
Anas discors
American widgeon
Mareca americana

Shoveler
Spatula clypeata
Ring-necked duck
Aythya collaris
Greater scaup
Aythya marila

Lesser scaup
Aythya affinis
Common goldeneye
Bucephala clangula
Bufflehead
Bucephala albeola
Hooded merganser
Lophodytes cucullatus
Common merganser
Mergus merganser
Red-breasted merganser
Mergus serrator
Goshawk
Accipiter gentilis
Sharp-shinned hawk
Accipiter striatus
Cooper's hawk
Accipiter cooperi
Red-tailed hawk
Buteo jamaicensis

Red-shouldered hawk
Buteo lineatus
Broad-winged hawk
Buteo platypterus
Golden eagle
Aquila chrysaetos
Bald eagle
Haliaeetus leucocephalus

Marsh hawk
Circus cyaneus
Osprey
Pandion haliaetus
Peregrine falcon
Falco peregrinus
Pigeon hawk
Falco columbarius
Sparrow hawk
Falco sparverius
Spruce grouse
Canachites canadensis
Ruffed grouse
Bonasa umbellus
Willow ptarmigan
Lagopus lagopus
Sharp-tailed grouse
Pedioecetes phasianellus
Sandhill crane
Grus canadensis
Virginia rail
Rallus limicola
Sora
Porzana carolina
Yellow rail
Coturnicops noveboracensis
American coot
Fulica americana
Semipalpated plover
Charadrius semipalmatus
Killdeer
Charadrius vociferus
American woodcock
Philohela minor
Common snipe
Capella gallinago
Upland plover
Bartramia longicauda
Spotted sandpiper
Acititus macularia
Solitary sandpiper
Tringa solitaria
Greater yellowlegs
Totanus melanoleucus
Lesser yellowlegs
Totanus flavipes
Pectoral sandpiper
Erolia melanotos
Least sandpiper
Erolia minutilla
Short-billed dowitcher
Limnodromus griseus
Semipalmated sandpiper
Ereunetes pusillus

Hudsonian godwit
Limosa haemastica

Northern phalarope
Lobipes lobatus

Herring gull
Larus argentatus

Ring-billed gull
Larus delawarensis

Bonaparte's gull
Larus philadelphia

Arctic tern
Sterna paradisaea

Black tern
Chidonias niger

Black guillemot
Cepphus grylle

Mourning dove
Zenaidura macroura

Black-billed cuckoo
Coccyzus erthropthalmus

Great horned owl
Bubo virginianus

Hawk owl
Surnia ulula

Barred owl
Strix varia

Great gray owl
Strix nebulosa

Long-eared owl
Asio otus

Short-eared owl
Asio flammeus

Boreal owl
Aegolius funereus

Saw-whet owl
Aegolius acadicus

Whip-poor-will
Caprimulgus vociferus

Common nighthawk
Chordeiles minor

Chimney swift
Chaetura pelagica

Ruby-throated hummingbird
Archilochus colubris

Belted kingfisher
Megaceryle alcyon

Yellow-bellied sapsucker
Sphyrapicus varius

Hairy woodpecker
Dendrocopos villosus

Downy woodpecker
Dendrocopos pubescens

Black-backed three-toed
woodpecker
Picoides arcticus

Northern three-toed
woodpecker
Picoides tridactylus

Eastern kingbird
Tyrannus tyrannus

Great crested flycatcher
Myiarchus crinitus

Eastern phoebe
Sayornis phoebe

Yellow-bellied flycatcher
Empidonax flaviventris

Traill's flycatcher
Empidonax traillii

Least flycatcher
Empidonax minimus

Eastern wood pewee
Contopus virens

Olive-sided flycatcher
Nuttallornis borealis

Horned lark
Eremophila alpestris

Tree swallow
Iridoprocne bicolor

Bank swallow
Riparia riparia

Barn swallow
Hirundo rustica

Cliff swallow
Petrochelidon pyrrhonota

Purple martin
Progne subis

Canada jay
Perisoreus canadensis

Blue jay
Cyanocitta cristata

Common raven
Corvus corax

Common crow
Corvus brachyrhynchos

Black-capped chickadee
Parus atricapillus

Boreal chickadee
Parus hudsonicus

White-breasted nuthatch
Sitta carolinensis

Red- breasted nuthatch
Sitta canadensis

Brown creeper
Certhia familiaris

House wren
Troglodytes aedon

Winter wren
Troglodytes troglodytes

Long-billed marsh wren
Telmatodytes palustris

Short-billed marsh wren
Cistothorus platensis

Catbird
Dumetella carolinensis

Brown thrasher
Toxostoma rufum

Robin
Turdus migratorius

Wood thrush
Hylocichla mustelina

Hermit thrush
Hylocichla guttata

Swainson's thrush
Hylocichla ustulata

Gray-cheeked thrush
Hylocichla minima

Veery
Hylocichla fuscescens

Eastern bluebird
Sialia sialis

Golden-crowned kinglet
Regulus satrapa

Ruby-crowned kinglet
Regulus calendula

Water pipit
Anthus spinoletta

Bohemian waxwing
Bombycilla garrulus

Cedar waxwing
Bombycilla cedrorum

Northern shrike
Lanius excubitor

Loggerhead shrike
Lanius ludovicianus

Common starling
Sturnus vulgaris

Solitary vireo
Vireo solitarius

Red-eyed vireo
Vireo olivaceus

Golden-winged warbler
Vermivora chrysoptera

Tennessee warbler
Vermivora peregrina

Orange-crowned warbler
Vermivora celata

Nashville warbler
Vermivora ruficapilla

Parula warbler
Parula americana

Yellow warbler
Dendroica petechia

Magnolia warbler
Dendroica magnolia

Cape May warbler
Dendroica tigrina

Black-throated blue warbler
Dendroica caerulescens

Myrtle warbler
Dendroica coronata

Black-throated green warbler
Dendroica virens

Blackburnian warbler
Dendroica fusca

Chestnut-sided warbler
Dendroica pensylvanica
Bay-breasted warbler
Dendroica castanea
Blackpoll warbler
Dendroica striata
Pine warbler
Dendroica pinus
Palm warbler
Dendroica palmarum
Ovenbird
Seiurus aurocapillus
Connecticut warbler
Oporornis agilis
Mourning warbler
Oporornis philadelphia
Yellowthroat
Geothlypis trichas
Wilson's warbler
Wilsonia pusilla

Canada warbler
Wilsonia canadensis
American redstart
Setophaga ruticilla
House sparrow
Passer domesticus
Baltimore oriole
Icterus galbula
Rusty blackbird
Euphagus carolinus
Grackle
Quiscalus quiscula
Brown-headed cowbird
Molothrus ater
Scarlet tanager
Piranga olivacea
Rose-breasted grosbeak
Pheucticus ludovicianus
Indigo bunting
Passerina cyanea
Evening grosbeak
Hesperiphona vespertina
Purple finch
Carpodacus purpureus

Pine grosbeak
Pinicola enucleator
Common redpoll
Acanthis flammea
Pine siskin
Spinus pinus
American goldfinch
Spinus tristis
White-winged crossbill
Loxia leucoptera
Rufous-sided towhee
Pipilo erythrophthalmus
Savannah sparrow
Passerculus sandwichensis
Vesper sparrow
Pooecetes gramineus
Slate-colored junco
Junco hyemalis
Tree sparrow
Spizella arborea
Chipping sparrow
Spizella passerina
White-crowned sparrow
Zonotrichia leucophrys
White-throated sparrow
Zonotrichia albicollis

Fox sparrow
Passerella iliaca
Lincoln's sparrow
Melospiza lincolnii
Swamp sparrow
Melospiza georgiana
Song sparrow
Melospiza melodia

MAMMALS
Common shrew
Sorex cinereus
Smoky shrew
Sorex fumeus
Water shrew
Sorex palustris

Pygmy shrew
Microsorex hoyi
Big short-tailed shrew
Blarina brevicauda
Star-nosed mole
Condylura cristata
Little brown bat
Myotis lucifugus
Silver-haired bat
Lasionycteris noctivagans
Big brown bat
Eptesicus fuscus
Hoary bat
Lasiurus cinereus
Snowshoe hare
Lepus americanus
Artic hare
Lepus arcticus
Eastern gray squirrel
Sciurus carolinensis
Red squirrel
Tamiasciurus hudsonicus
Woodchuck
Marmota monax
Eastern chipmunk
Tamiius striatus
Least chipmunk
Eutamius minimus

Northern flying squirrel
Glaucomys sabrinus
Beaver
Castor canadensis
Deer mouse
Peromyscus maniculatus
Ungava varying lemming
Dicrostonyx hudsonius
Bog lemming
Synaptomys cooperi
Northern lemming mouse
Synaptomys borealis
Red-backed mouse
Clethrionomys gapperi

Meadow vole
Microtus pennsylvanicus
Muskrat
Ondatra zivethicus
Meadow jumping mouse
Zapus hudsonius
Woodland jumping mouse
Napaeozapus insignis
Porcupine
Erethizon dorsatum
Timber wolf
Canis lupis
Arctic fox
Alopex lagopus
Red fox
Vulpes vulpes
Black bear
Ursus americanus
Raccoon
Procyon lotor
Ermine
Mustela erminia
Least weasel
Mustela rixosa
Mink
Mustela vison
Marten
Martes americana

Fisher
Martes pennanti
Wolverine
Gulo luscus
Skunk
Mephitis mephitis
Canada lynx
Lynx canadensis
Bobcat
Lynx rufus
White-tailed deer
Odocoileus virginianus
Moose
Alces alces
Caribou
Rangifer tarandus

REGIONAL MAPS AND INFORMATION

Large-scale maps and other information on the Canadian Shield can be obtained at moderate cost from: Department of Mines and Natural Resources, Norquay Building, Winnipeg; Department of Lands and Forests, Parliament Building, Quebec City; Quebec Department of Natural Resources, 1620-1640 Boul. de l'Entente, Quebec 6; Department of Lands and Forests, Room 2431, Ontario Government Buildings, Queen's Park, Toronto; Department of Energy, Mines and Resources, 601 Booth Street, Ottawa. A selection of film strips and slides is available from: National Film Board, P.O. Box 6100, Montreal 3, Quebec.

BIBLIOGRAPHY

REGIONAL

BEALS, C. S. AND SHENSTONE, D. A. (eds.)
Science, History and Hudson Bay (2 vols.)
Ottawa: Department of Energy, Mines and Resources, 1968.

BERTON, PIERRE.
The Mysterious North.
New York: Alfred A. Knopf, 1956.

BLADEN, V. W. (ed.)
Canadian Population and Northern Development.
Toronto: University of Toronto Press, 1962.

HARDY, W. G. (ed.)
Alberta, A Natural History.
Edmonton: M. G. Hurtig, 1967.

Mid-Canada Development Corridor . . . A Concept.
Thunder Bay: Lakehead University, 1967.

MOWAT, FARLEY.
Canada North.
Toronto: McClelland and Stewart, 1967.

Proceedings: Fourth National Northern Development Conference.
Edmonton: Alberta & Northwest Chamber of Mines and Resources and the Edmonton Chamber of Commerce, 1967.

REA, KENNETH.
The Political Economy of the Canadian North.
Toronto: University of Toronto Press, 1968.

RICHARDSON, SIR JOHN.
Arctic Searching Expedition with an Appendix of the Physical Geography of North America. (2 vols.)
London: Longman, Brown, Green & Longman's, 1851.

ROBINSON, J. LEWIS.
Resources of the Canadian Shield.
Toronto: Methuen Publications, 1969.

SMITH, I. N. (ed.)
The Unbelievable Land.
Ottawa: Queen's Printer, 1966.

VON STEENSEL, MAJA (ed.)
People of Light and Dark.
Ottawa: Queen's Printer, 1966.

WILSON, CLIFFORD (ed.)
North of 55°.
Toronto: The Ryerson Press, 1954.

GEOLOGY

Age Determinations and Geological Studies.
Ottawa: Geological Survey of Canada, Paper 66-17, 1967.

ALCOCK, F. J.
A Century in the History of the Geological Survey of Canada.
Ottawa: Geological Survey of Canada, Paper 47-1, 1948.

Canadian Upper Mantle Report, 1967.
Ottawa: Geological Survey of Canada, Paper 67-41, 1967.

CLARK, THOMAS H. and STEARN, COLIN W.
The Geological Evolution of North America.
New York: Harper and Row, 1962.

FINDLAY, D. C. and SMITH, C. H.
The Muskox Drilling Project.
Ottawa: Geological Survey of Canada, Paper 64-44, 1965.

GARLAND, G. D.
Continental Drift.
Toronto: Univ. of Toronto Press, 1966.

GASKELL, T. F. (ed.)
The Earth's Mantle.
London: Academic Press Ltd., 1967.

GILLULY, JAMES (ed.)
Origin of Granite.
Ann Arbor, Michigan: The Geological Society of America, Memoir 28, 1953.

JENNESS, S. E. (ed.)
Contributions to Geological Exploration in Canada.
Ottawa: Geological Survey of Canada, Paper 66-42, 1966.

JENNESS, S. E. (ed.)
Guidebook: Geology of Parts of Eastern Ontario and Western Quebec.
Geological Association of Canada, 1967.

KAY, G. M. and COLBERT, EDWIN.
Stratigraphy and Life History.
New York: Wiley, 1965.

LOGAN, WILLIAM.
Geology of Canada.
Ottawa: Geological Survey of the Province of Canada, 1863.

OSBORNE, F. F.
Geochronology in Canada.
Toronto: Royal Society of Canada, Special Publication No. 8, 1964.

PEARL, RICHARD M.
Rocks and Minerals.
New York: Barnes & Noble, 1956.

RAGUIN, E.
The Geology of Granite.
New York: Wiley, 1965.

RAMSEY, W. L. and BURCKLEY, R.A.
Modern Earth Science.
New York: Holt, Rinehart, Winston, 1965.

RAPPORT, SAMUEL and WRIGHT, HELEN (eds.)
The Crust of the Earth.
New York: The New American Library of World Literature, 1955.

SABINA, ANN P.
*Rock and Mineral Collecting in Canada:
Volume II.*
Ottawa: Geological Survey of Canada, 1965.

STEVENSON, J. S. (ed.)
The Tectonics of the Canadian Shield.
Toronto: Royal Society of Canada,
Special Publication No. 4, 1962.

STOKES, WILLIAM LEE.
Essentials of Earth History.
Englewood Cliffs, New Jersey:
Prentice-Hall, 1960.

THOMSON, JAMES E.
Geology of the Sudbury Basin.
Toronto: Ontario Department of Mines, 1952.

WILSON, J. TUZO.
*The Origin of Continents and
Precambrian History.*
Toronto: The Royal Society of Canada,
Vol. XLIII, Series 3, 1949.

WILSON, J. TUZO.
*Some Aspects of Geophysics in Canada,
with Special Reference to Structural
Research in the Canadian Shield.*
American Geophysical Union, Transactions:
Vol. 29, No. 5, 1948; Vol. 30, No. 3, 1949;
Vol. 31, No. 1, 1950.

PERIODICAL

WILSON, J. TUZO.
"Some Major Structures of the Canadian Shield."
Canadian Mining and Metallurgical Bulletin,
Vol. 43, No. 451, 1949.

PLANTS

AHMADJIAN, V.
The Lichen Symbiosis.
Waltham, Massachusetts: Blaisdell, 1967.

BAKUZIS, E. V. and HANSEN, H. L.
Balsam Fir.
Minneapolis: Univ. of Minnesota Press, 1965.

BALDWIN, W. K. W.
*Botanical Excursion to the Boreal Forest
Region in North Quebec and Ontario.*
Ottawa: Dept. of Northern Affairs, 1962.

BALDWIN, W. K. W.
*Plants of the Clay Belt of Northern
Ontario and Quebec.*
Ottawa: National Museum of Canada,
Bulletin No. 156, 1958.

CUNNINGHAM, G. C.
Forest Flora of Canada.
Ottawa: Department of Northern Affairs, 1958.

DUTILLY, PERE ARTHÈME.
*Coup d'Oeil sur la Flore Subarctique
du Quebec.*
Washington: Catholic Univ. of America, 1948.

EYRE, S. R.
Vegetation and Soils.
London: Edward Arnold Publishers, 1968.

Forest Regions of Canada.
Ottawa: Department of Northern Affairs
and National Resources, Bulletin 123,
Forestry Branch, 1959.

GLEASON, H. A. and CRONQUIST, A.
The Natural Geography of the Plants.
New York: Columbia Univ. Press, 1964.

HALE, M. E.
The Biology of the Lichens.
London: Edward Arnold, 1967.

HALE, M. E.
*A Guide to the Lichens of Eastern
North America.*
Washington: Smithsonian Institute, 1961.

HARPER, F.
*Plant and Animal Associations in the
Interior of Ungava Peninsula.*
Kansas: Museum of Natural History,
Miscellaneous Publications No. 38, 1964.

MARIE-VICTORIN, FRÈRE.
Flora Laurentienne.
Montreal: Les Presses de l'Universite
de Montreal, 1964.

MCCORMICK, J.
The Life of the Forest.
Toronto: McGraw-Hill, 1963.

MONTGOMERY, F. H.
Plants from Sea to Sea.
Toronto: Ryerson Press, 1966.

Native Trees of Canada.
Ottawa: Department of Forestry, 1963.

PORSILD, A. E.
Plant Life in the Arctic.
Ottawa: National Museum of Canada,
Miscellaneous Publications No. 74, 1951.

*Proceedings of the First Canadian
Conference on Permafrost.*
Ottawa: National Research Council, 1963.

RITCHIE, J. C.
The Vegetation of Northern Manitoba.
Montreal: Arctic Institute of North America,
Technical Paper No. 3, 1959.

ROWE, J. S.
*Factors Influencing White Spruce Repro-
duction in Manitoba and Saskatchewan.*
Ottawa: Forest Research Division,
Technical Note No. 3, 1955.

TAYLOR, R. L. and LUDWIG, R. A.
The Evolution of Canada's Flora.
Toronto: University of Toronto Press, 1966.

WILTON, W. C.
The Forests of Labrador.
Ottawa: Dept. of Forestry,
Publication 1066, 1965.

PERIODICALS

DANSEREAU, P. and SEGADAS–VIANNA, F.
"Ecological Study of the Peat Bogs
of Eastern North America."
Canadian Journal of Botany, Vol. 30, 1952.

DEEVEY, E. S.
"Bogs."
Scientific American, Vol. 199, 1958.

HEINSELMAN, M. L.
"Forest Sites, Bog Processes and Peatland
Types in the Glacial Lake Agassiz
Region, Minnesota."
Ecological Monographs, Vol. 33, P.327, 1963.

HILLS, G. A.
"The Soils of the Canadian Shield."
Agricultural Institute Review,
Vol. 15, No. 2, 1960.

HUSTICH, I.
"The Boreal Limits of Conifers."
Acta Geographica, Vol. 15, No. 3, 1954.

HUSTICH, I.
"The Lichen Woodlands in Labrador."
Acta Geographica, Vol. 12, No. 1, 1951.

LAMB, I. M.
"Lichens."
Scientific American, Vol. 201, 1959.

LA ROI, G. H.
"Ecological Studies in the Boreal
Spruce-Fir Forests of the North
American Taiga."
Ecological Monographs, Vol. 37, P.227, 1967.

ANIMALS

BENT, A. C.
Life Histories of North American Warblers.
New York: Dover Publications Inc., 1963.

BLEAKNEY, J. S.
*A Zoogeographical Study of the Amphibians
and Reptiles of Eastern Canada.*
Ottawa: National Museum of Canada,
Bulletin No. 155, 1958.

BOULIERE, FRANCOIS.
The Natural History of Mammals.
New York: Alfred A. Knopf, 1964.

CHAPMAN, F. M.
The Warblers of North America.
New York: Dover Publications, 1968.

DORST, JEAN.
The Migration of Birds.
Cambridge: Riverside Press, 1963.

ELTON, CHARLES.
Voles, Mice and Lemmings.
Toronto: Oxford Press, 1942.

GRIFFIN, D. R.
Bird Migration.
Garden City: Doubleday, 1964.

GRISCOM, L. and SPRUNT, A. JR. (eds.)
The Warblers of North America.
New York: Gevin-Adair, 1957.

KEITH, L. B.
Wildlife's Ten-Year Cycle.
Madison: University of Wisconsin Press, 1963.

KENDIEGH, S. CHARLES.
Nesting Behavior of Wood Warblers.
Wilson Bulletin 57, 1945.

KENDIEGH, S. CHARLES.
*Bird Population Studies in the Coniferous
Forest Biome during a Spruce Budworm Outbreak.*
Toronto: Ontario Dept. of Lands and Forests,
Biological Bulletin No. 1, 1947.

LANSDOWNE, V. F. and LIVINGSTON, J. A.
Birds of the Northern Forest.
Toronto: McClelland & Stewart, 1966.

LANHAM, URL.
The Insects.
New York: Columbia Univ. Press, 1964.

LAWRENCE, L.
The Lovely and the Wild.
Toronto: McGraw-Hill, 1968.

MANNING, T. H.
The Northern Red-Backed Mouse.
Ottawa: National Museum of Canada,
Bulletin No. 144, 1956.

OLDROYD, H.
Natural History of the Flies.
London: Weidenfeld and Nicolson, 1964.

OLIVER, D. R.
Insects.
Ottawa: Department of Agriculture, 1967.

PETERSON, R. L.
The Mammals of Eastern Canada.
Toronto: Oxford Univ. Press, 1966.

PIMLOTT, G. H.
The Ecology of the Timber Wolf.
Toronto: Ontario Dept. of Lands
and Forests, 1969.

PRUITT, W. O.
Animals of the North.
New York: Harper & Row, 1960.

RUE, LEONARD LEE.
The World of the White-tailed Deer.
Philadelphia: J. B. Lippincott, 1962.

RUE, LEONARD LEE.
The World of the Beaver.
Philadelphia: J. B. Lippincott, 1964.

RUTTER, R. J. and PIMLOTT, D. H.
The World of the Wolf.
Philadelphia: J. B. Lippincott, 1968.

SCOTT, W. B.
Freshwater Fishes of Eastern Canada.
Toronto: Univ. of Toronto Press, 1957.

VAN WORMER, JOE.
The World of the Black Bear.
Philadelphia: J. B. Lippincott, 1966.

WYNNE-EDWARDS, V. C.
*Animal Dispersion in Relation to
Social Behavior.*
New York: Hafner, 1962.

YOUNG, J. Z.
The Life of the Mammals.
London: Oxford, 1957.

PERIODICALS

DAVIES, D. M. and PETERSON, D. G.
"Black Flies."
Canadian Journal of Zoology, Vol. 34, 1956.

DOWNES, J. A.
"Arctic Insects and their Environment."
Canadian Entomologist, Vol. 96, 1964.

MATTHEWS, L. HARRISON.
"Hibernation in Mammals and Birds."
British Medical Bulletin, Vol. 17, No. 1, 1961.

MUNROE, E.
"Canada as an Environment for Insect Life."
Canadian Entomologist, Vol. 88, 1956.

PRUITT, W. O.
"Animals in the Snow."
Scientific American, January, 1960.

"Symposium on Animal Populations."
Journal of Wildlife Management,
Vol. 18, 1954.

MISCELLANEOUS

CAMU, PIERRE, WEEKS, E. P. and SAMETZ, A. W.
Economic Geography of Canada.
Toronto: Macmillan of Canada, 1964.

DARLING, F. F. and MILTON, J. P. (eds.)
*Future Environments of North America:
Transformation of a Continent.*
Garden City, New Jersey: The Natural
History Press, 1966.

ELLIS, ELEANOR A.
The Northern Cookbook.
Ottawa: Department of Indian Affairs
and Northern Development, 1967.

GENTILCORE, R. L.
Canada's Changing Geography.
Scarborough: Prentice-Hall, 1967.

HOFFMAN, ARNOLD.
Free Gold.
New York: Rinehart and Co., 1947.

LANG, A. H.
Prospecting in Canada (3rd edition).
Ottawa: Geological Survey of Canada,
Economic Geology Series No. 7, 1956.

LOEBSACK, THEO.
Our Atmosphere.
New York: The American Library of
World Literature, Inc., 1961.

MILLER, A. AUSTIN.
The Skin of the Earth.
London: University Paperback Series, 1964.

MILNE, LORUS J. and MILNE, MARGERY J.
The Biotic World and Man (2nd edition).
Englewood Cliffs, New Jersey:
Prentice-Hall, 1958.

ODUM, EUGENE P.
Ecology.
New York: Holt, Rinehart and Winston, 1963.

PUTNAM, D. F. and KERR, D. F.
A Regional Geography of Canada.
Toronto: J. M. Dent & Sons, Rev. 1966.

PUTNAM, D. F. et al.
Canadian Regions.
Toronto: J. M. Dent & Sons, 1967.

Resources for Tomorrow Conference
Ottawa: Queen's Printer.
Vols. 1 and 2 Background Papers, 1961.
Vol. 3 Proceedings, 1962.

SANDERSON, IVAN T.
The Continent We Live On.
New York: Random House, 1961.

The Climate of Canada.
Toronto: Meteorological Branch Air Services,
Department of Transport, 1967.

WARKENTIN, JOHN, (ed.)
Canada: A Geographical Interpretation.
Toronto: Methuen Publications, 1968.

INDEX

ACKNOWLEDGEMENTS

The author and editors wish to acknowledge with gratitude the advice and assistance of: Dr. I. M. Brodo, National Museum of Canada, Ottawa – on lichens; Dr. D. M. Davies, Dept. of Biology, McMaster University – on black flies; Dr. Michael R. Dence, Div'n. of Gravity, Observatories Branch, Department of Energy, Mines and Resources – on fossil meteor craters; Dr. Alan Goodwin, Dept. of Geology, University of Toronto – on Precambrian volcanics; Dr. W. H. Gunn, Federation of Ontario Naturalists – on warblers; Dr. L. B. Keith, Dept. of Wildlife Ecology, University of Wisconsin – on the ten-year cycle in wildlife populations; Lewis Moyd, Curator of Minerals, National Museum of Canada – on minerals; Dr. John G. Oughton, University of Guelph – on ecology; Dr. D. H. Pimlott, Department of Zoology, University of Toronto – on Shield mammals; Dr. J. H. Sparling, Dept. of Botany, University of Toronto – on muskeg and bog formation; Dr. J. Tuzo Wilson, Erindale College, University of Toronto – on mantle convection and continental drift; Dr. H. Wynne-Edwards, Department of Geology, Queen's University – on the Grenville Province; Dr. Walter Zingg, The Hospital for Sick Children, Toronto – on hibernation in birds and mammals. There are other debts: to the park naturalists of Algonquin Provincial Park, and to the leaders and members of Geological Field Trip No. 1, August-September, 1967, sponsored by the Geological Association of Canada and the Mineralogical Association of Canada, for patient tutelage in the field; and to Dr. L. W. Morley, Mrs. Lewis Moyd, and no fewer than twenty-two geologists of the Geological Survey of Canada, who were generous beyond measure with their time, their ideas, their own research and their good auspices. Particular thanks must also go to J. R. Janes of Brock University, a cheerful and indefatigable tutor in Precambrian geology and the earth sciences, and to Miss Libby Oughton, a researcher who insists on getting things right.

PICTURE CREDITS

Order of appearance in the text of pictures listed here is left to right, top to bottom.

Cover/Bill Brooks
1/Victor Crich
2-3/Bill Brooks
4-5/Paul Baich
8/Walter Murray
20-51/Bill Brooks
61/Victor Crich
62/Bill Brooks
63/Alma Carmichael, Bill Brooks, Bill Brooks, T. W. Hall
64-87/Bill Brooks
89/Dr. George K. Peck
90/Victor Crich
91/Dr. George K. Peck, Dr. George K. Peck, Ken Carmichael
92/Dr. George K. Peck, Dr. George K. Peck, Ken Carmichael, Dr. George K. Peck
93/Dr. George K. Peck
96/Helen Sutton
98/Bill Brooks
103-108/Helen Sutton
112/Dr. George K. Peck
115-135/Bill Brooks
136/John de Visser
138-141/National Air Photo Library

This book was produced entirely in Canada by
Mono Lino Typesetting Co. Limited: *Typesetting;* Herzig Sommerville Limited: *Film Separation*
Ashton-Potter Limited: *Printing;* T. H. Best Printing Co. Limited: *Binding*
Typefaces: Times New Roman and Univers. Paper: 65 lb. Georgian Offset Smooth

PRINTED IN CANADA

A B C D E F 73 72 71 70